GENERATING ECONOMIC CYCLES

Also published in

Reprints Of Economic Classics

By Henry Ludwell Moore

Economic Cycles Their Law & Cause [1914]
Forecasting The Yield & The Price Of Cotton [1917]
Laws Of Wages [1911]
Synthetic Economics [1929]

GENERATING ECONOMIC CYCLES

BY

HENRY LUDWELL MOORE

PROFESSOR OF POLITICAL ECONOMY IN COLUMBIA UNIVERSITY

" To this the King replied, that he who worried
so anxiously about the end of a piece of work
would never make a beginning in anything."

BENVENUTO CELLINI.

REPRINTS OF ECONOMIC CLASSICS

AUGUSTUS M. KELLEY · PUBLISHERS
NEW YORK · 1967

FIRST EDITION 1923

(New York: The Macmillan Company, 1923)

Reprinted 1967 by

AUGUSTUS M. KELLEY PUBLISHERS

Library of Congress Catalogue Card Number
65-26370

PRINTED IN THE UNITED STATES OF AMERICA
by SENTRY PRESS, NEW YORK, N. Y. 10019

TO

THE MEMORY OF MY FATHER

CONTENTS

PAGE

Preface ix

CHAPTER I

INTRODUCTION

A Clue to the Economic Maze 1
Three Types of Contemporary Theories of Cycles . . 2
Method and Results 5
Reservations 11

CHAPTER II

GENERATING CYCLES OF PRODUCTS AND PRICES

The Correlation of Crop Yields and Crop Prices . . . 18
Generating Cycles of Products 24
The Derived Cycles of Prices 26
Cycles in the Products of Mines 28
Cycles in the Production of the Raw Materials of Manufacture 32

CHAPTER III

· GENERATING CYCLES REFLECTED IN A CENTURY OF PRICES

Data and Method 42
An Analysis of a Century of Prices 47
Crop Cycles as Generating Cycles 55

CHAPTER IV

THE ORIGIN OF THE EIGHT-YEAR GENERATING CYCLE

Economic Cycles 70
Meteorological Cycles 76
The Cause of the Eight-Year Generating Cycle . . . 88

Contents

CHAPTER V

THE EIGHT-YEAR GENERATING CYCLE IN RELATION TO ITS PHYSICAL CAUSE

	PAGE
Recent Theories of the Sun	104
Influence of the New Physics	111
The Rôle of Venus	121

PREFACE

AMONG the rare books in the library where I am writing there is a first edition of Galileo's treatise *Dialogo sopra i due massimi sistemi del mondo, Tolemaico e Copernicano.* This was the work that brought him before the Roman Inquisition. By the Holy Office he was convicted "of believing and holding the doctrines—false and contrary to the Holy and Divine Scriptures—that the Sun is the centre of the world, and that it does not move from east to west, and that the Earth does move and is not the centre of the world; also that an opinion can be held and supported as probable after it has been declared and decreed contrary to the Holy Scriptures," and he was required by the Holy Office to "abjure, curse, and detest the aforesaid errors."

Intolerance of unwonted views was not limited to the Holy Office. Galileo himself could close the windows of his mind and vent his critical scorn upon an adventurous colleague. In the fourth chapter of his fatal book there is a discussion of the theory of terrestrial tides which was the occasion of Galileo's treating with disdain the suggestion of Kepler that the tides are dependent upon the attraction of the Moon. To Galileo this seemed an explanation by an appeal to "occult Qualities and to such like vain Imaginations, that are so far from being, or being possible to be Causes of the Tide that on the contrary, the Tide is the cause of them, that is, of bringing them into the brains more apt for loquacity and ostentation than for the speculation and discovering of the more abstruse secrets of Nature; which kind of people, before they can be brought to pronounce that wise, ingenious, and modest sentence, *I know it not,* suffer to escape from their mouths and pens all manner of extravagancies." And he added: "But amongst all the famous men that have philosophated upon this admirable effect of Nature, I wonder more at Kepler than any of the rest, who being of a free and piercing wit, and having the motion ascribed to the Earth before him, hath for all that given ear and assent to the Moon's predominancy over the Water, and to the occult properties, and such like trifles." [1]

As far as it went Kepler's theory was undoubtedly correct and Galileo's ingenious attribution of the tides to a combination of complex motions of the Earth was incontestably wrong. And certainly Kepler was not to be blamed for the vagueness of his theory considering that it was expressed two centuries before the composition of the *Mécanique Céleste,* at a time when it was impossible for him to know the theory of gravitation, to become acquainted with the necessary mathematical tools of research, or to command the indispensable tidal observations.

We who are concerned with economic cycles—the tides in the affairs of men—may learn much from the subsequent history and theory of terrestrial tides. The theory of their cause passed from the stage of a promising speculation to that of a well-ordered working hypothesis when it took the rigid mathematical form

[1] The translation by Thomas Salisbury, 1661, pp. 406–407, 422.

in which it appears in the *Mécanique Céleste;* it passed to the stage of tested, working theory after tidal observations upon a vast scale had been collected, submitted to analysis, and the results found to be in agreement with the tidal theory; the method of research was statistical, and the mathematical instrument was the harmonic analysis; the course of progress in tidal forecasting was to isolate the primary cycles and then to approximate more accurate measurements by combining primary changes with minor disturbances; the primary cycles were shown to be the effects of cosmical causes, and these causes were not discredited when their effects were not immediately discernible over one-half of the Earth; the phases of lag and lead and the complication of cosmical causes with general terrestrial and local causes were found to give an increasingly accurate account of the observed phenomena.

These features in the theory and history of tides will probably be found to have their counterparts in the theory and history of economic cycles. Will the theory of the cosmical origin of generating cycles, like Kepler's theory of the cosmical origin of terrestrial tides, incur the scorn of eminent critics and receive an adequate development only after two hundred years?

GENERATING ECONOMIC CYCLES

CHAPTER I

INTRODUCTION

AN ancient fable teaches the wisdom of providing one's self with a clue before going into an unexplored labyrinth. We are in search of regular causes of economic fluctuations and before entering the tangled maze of changes, we wish to profit by the wisdom of the ancient myth and take with us a clue to the intricate disorder

A Clue to the Economic Maze

Such a clue to the general course of regular economic changes in the United States and to the causes in which they originate is given by the rhythmic changes in the weather. Figure 1 describes three fundamental general facts which, considering the dependence of agriculture upon the weather, suggest an originating source of economic regularities and may not wisely be ignored in a theory of economic cycles. The three facts revealed by Figure 1 are these:

(1) The annual rainfall in the United States considered as a unit fluctuated in clearly defined eight-year cycles during the forty years for which we have data, from 1881 to 1921;

(2) The rainfall of the Ohio Valley fluctuated in clearly defined eight-year cycles during the seventy-two years from 1839 to 1910;

(3) The cycles in the Ohio Valley were congruent with those in the United States considered as a unit.

The course of rainfall before 1839, when there were no meteorological records in the middle and western portions of the United States, may be a subject of dispute, and one may have individual doubts as to the course of rainfall in the unrealized future. But the revelations of the existing record of eighty-three years describe a sequence of regular natural changes of such magnitude and of such economic importance that the observant explorer in quest of economic regularities will not ignore their suggestiveness. They supply a clue to the intricate economic disorder.

Three Types of Contemporary Theories of Cycles

When the theory of economic cycles is completely worked out and the critical stages in its development are reviewed, there will be a grateful recognition of the helpfulness of Cournot's distinction between secular, cyclical, and random causes of change. This classification is an essential preliminary to a wise choice of methods of investigation, and there must be a marked difference in theories of cycles according to the degree in which the necessity of the segregation of causes is realized and methods appropriate to the three types of causes are devised.

The degree in which these exigencies are recognized

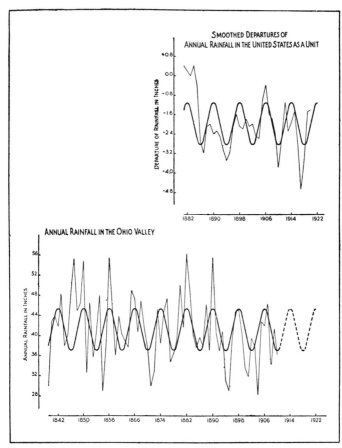

FIGURE 1
Cycles in the annual rainfall of the Ohio Valley and in the annual rainfall of the
United States as a unit.
Cycles in the United States: $y = -1.99 + 0.86 \sin (45°t + 42° 50')$, origin at 1881;
Cycles in the Ohio Valley: $y = 41.19 + 4.13 \sin (45°t + 310° 41')$, origin at 1839.

and met is a source of difference between three types of
contemporary theories of cycles:

In the first type there is a refusal to define the term,
economic or business cycle, otherwise than as a vague
general rhythm, a series of changes which returns at an

unspecified time upon itself. The treatment is not concerned with the academic segregation of causes nor with the pedantries of mathematical formulæ. No measures of correlated changes are carried out, and no definite clear-cut theory of cyclical causes is offered. Somehow, somewhen, some of the indices of business rise or fall, and somehow, somewhen, some other indices may follow. The possibility of forecasting is hinted, but in the best examples of this point of view there is prudent restraint in particularizing.

In the second of the typical current discussions of cycles there is a full realization of the need of separating causes and of seeking appropriate mathematical methods, but it introduces two embarrassing compromises: First, it proceeds upon the assumption that there are no known methods by which cyclical effects may be separated from random effects and accordingly attempts to treat as a whole the joint effect of cyclical and random causes; Secondly, it arbitrarily defines the combined effect as "the cycle." "The cycle," in this method of treatment, is the residue of the total effect under investigation after the secular trend has been eliminated. There is no further analysis of this residual quantity for the purpose of seeing whether it may not be composed, in part, of constituent cycles with separate causes, but it is forthwith used—and used often with success—as a means of practical forecasting.

The third typical theory of cycles assumes as its point of departure the necessity of segregating causes and the use of methods to decompose total effects into secular, cyclical, and random elements. The term cycle is mathematically defined with definite period, amplitude, and phase. The primary object of the theory is not to forecast but to establish the existence of real cycles and to trace the causes of the specifically cyclical elements in the total of economic changes. It distinguishes between a rational forecast and an empirical forecast. No rational forecast can be made until the manner of change in the various constituents of the full cause is discovered and their measured interrelations are known. Empirical forecasts of value may be made, and are made, from the known routine in the sequence of economic changes.

Method and Results

If the third type of theory with regard to the nature of cycles is allowed, then one is confronted with the problem of finding a method of determining whether a series of observations contains real cycles. Several technical methods, to which reference will be made in the following chapters, have been devised for this purpose; but without entering upon technicalities we may see that from the point of view of forecasting and controlling economic changes, the importance of a cycle is dependent upon its amplitude. A cycle may be real and yet practically negligible if its recurrent effects are small. This very practical consideration suggests the method to adopt in order to discover significant cycles. It is obvious that whatever may be the mathematical justification of the procedure it is practically important to know which cycle will show the largest amplitude in the given data, and this may be ascertained by finding the amplitudes of trial cycles with periods between limits that will be determined by the problem in hand.

Suppose, for example, we wished to know what cycle with period between three and twelve years would give

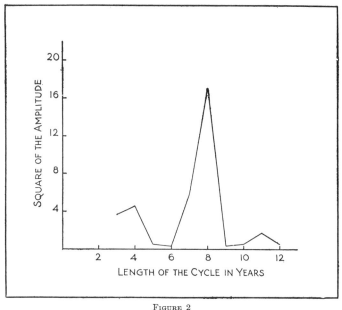

FIGURE 2
The periodogram of annual rainfall in the Ohio Valley, 1839–1910.

the largest amplitude in the annual rainfall of the Ohio Valley for the interval of seventy-two years from 1839 to 1910. The results of the computation according to the method that has just been sketched are graphed in Figure 2. On the horizontal line the lengths of the various trial periods are measured, and on the corresponding perpendicular lines are plotted the squares of the respective amplitudes. It is clear from Figure 2 that the cycle with a period in the neighborhood of eight years is by far the most important. The graph is given in Figure 1. The mean annual rainfall in the Ohio Valley is 41.19 inches, and the amplitude of the eight-year cycle is 4.13 inches. The range of the eight-year cycle, which is twice its amplitude, is 8.26 inches or twenty per cent of the annual rainfall. The tremendous importance of much smaller variations in precipitation is being increasingly emphasized by the findings of the growing science of agricultural meteorology.

The cyclical regularity in the variations of the rainfall in the Ohio Valley for the seventy-two years from 1839 to 1910 was first announced [1] in 1914, and as the computations rested upon the records of only three stations, Cincinnati, Portsmouth, and Marietta, there was a very reasonable skepticism as to the reality of the eight-year cycle. One might concede that the measurements of rainfall at the three stations show the eight-year cycle for nine consecutive periods in the seventy-two years, and yet deny the economic importance of the cycle on the ground that no evidence has been submitted to show its presence in the whole of the United States. This perfectly legitimate objection must be met, and we shall attempt to meet it by conducting an independent inquiry that will serve as a severe test of the reality and generality of the eight-year cycle. We shall use all available data for the whole of the United States; we shall start with no prejudice with regard to

---

[1] *Economic Cycles: Their Law and Cause*, 1914. The data are given in that work, p. 32.

the existence of a cycle of definite period; we shall simply inquire, if there be an important cycle with period between three and twelve years, what the length is; and then we shall compare the findings with those that were obtained for the Ohio Valley.

In 1922 Professor Alfred J. Henry of the *United States Weather Bureau* published [1] an article which for the first time supplied rainfall data relating to the United States as a unit. Professor Henry's object was to show that there is no ground whatever for the recent claim that rainfall in the United States follows the eleven-year sun-spot cycle, and he sought to make his criticism as convincing as possible by arraying against the sun-spot argument the vast material collected by the *Weather Bureau*.

The records that were utilized by Professor Henry were drawn from about two hundred individual *Weather Bureau* stations grouped into twenty climatic districts embracing the whole of the United States.[2]

[1] *Monthly Weather Review*, March, 1922, p. 130.

[2] These details Professor Henry gave me in a letter of December 29, 1922. After Professor Henry published his article he discovered that a number of errors had crept into his data and computations and he very kindly sent to me, in December, 1922, his corrected table of rainfall departures for the forty years from 1881 to 1921. In Table I of the Appendix to this chapter are listed Professor Henry's original data as they appeared in the *Monthly Weather Review*, March, 1922, p. 130, and his corrected data as they were sent to me in December, 1922. In both cases Professor Henry smoothed the raw data by means of the formula $b = \frac{1}{4}(a + 2b + c)$ where b was the value of the middle year in each consecutive series of three years.

The curve in Figure 1 for the rainfall in the whole of the United States was computed from Professor Henry's corrected data. The curve that was published in my paper on "An Eight-Year Rainfall Cycle," which appeared in the *Monthly Weather Review*, July, 1922, was based upon Professor Henry's uncorrected figures and fitted the data slightly better than the curve that is given in Figure 1.

If, now, we analyse Professor Henry's data [1]—which run from 1881 to 1920—with a view to discovering whether there are important cycles in the rainfall of the United States as a unit, we obtain these surprising results:

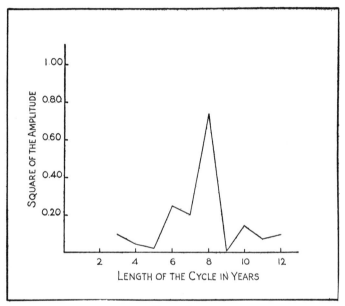

FIGURE 3
The periodogram of annual rainfall departures in the United States as a unit.
1881–1920.

(1) Figure 3 shows that if there is an important real cycle within the limits of three and twelve years in the rainfall of the United States as a unit, its period is about eight years;

(2) Figure 1 shows that when the equation to the eight-year rainfall cycle in the United States is

[1] The data are given in Table I of the Appendix to this chapter. The figures in the column marked "Corrected Data" were used in the computation.

computed its maxima are, within the limits of the errors of observation, coincident with the maxima of the eight-year rainfall cycle in the Ohio Valley, which, in 1914, was found to have persisted throughout nine consecutive periods;

(3) The amplitude of the eight-year cycle in the United States is relatively so large that it accounts for 42 per cent of the total variability of the annual rainfall. This result is obtained by taking the ratio of the amplitude of the eight-year cycle to the mean of the annual rainfall departures irrespective of their signs.

These meteorological facts raise important questions in the extremes of the hierarchy of the sciences. If the regularities that have been observed are not accidental they are probably cosmical in origin, and one of the leading questions they suggest relates to the astronomic and physical agents by means of which they may be produced. The fourth and fifth of the following chapters enter into the details of this question.

While solar physics must be looked to for an explanation of the weather regularities, the regularities themselves are the starting point of the economist's inquiry into cyclical economic changes. He wishes to know whether the observed cyclical recurrence of rainfall with its large amplitude may not originate agricultural cycles which, in turn, generate the cycles of production and the cycles of prices with which the economist is more immediately concerned. The second, third, and fourth of the ensuing chapters treat of the details of this economic problem.

Reservations

The primary purpose of this Essay is to show that a known natural cause originates an agricultural cycle which in turn generates other economic cycles. The perturbations in the ultimate cycles are not discussed, and these perturbations will doubtless be traced in part to natural, and, in part, to psychical and social origins. Because one element of the weather, rainfall, has been seized upon and its effects have been tracked into remote regions, it does not follow that temperature,[1] sunshine, and wind are regarded as negligible. Because a natural eight-year cycle has been isolated is no reason for denying the possible existence of other natural cycles, major or minor. Because some regularities in economic changes have been shown to originate in natural causes, it would be most unphilosophic to claim that the effects of the known regular causes may not be partially or totally offset by the effects of other causes, natural or social, regular or fortuitous. The object has been to find one cause and to follow its effects into their ultimate ramifications.

However ingenious may be the mathematical methods that are used to isolate periodicities, there will always be a healthy skepticism as to the reality of the cycles unless true causes are adduced. Mere empirical regularities are always suspect. While, therefore, in the quest of cycles, I have always tried to scrutinize the data by means of impartial mathematical devices, I have not remained content with empirical results but

[1] *Forecasting the Yield and the Price of Cotton*, 1917.

have pressed on in search of real causes. The pursuit has led into meteorology, astronomy, and solar physics, where I may possibly have gone astray. But whatever uncertainties may be felt with regard to these adventures into natural science, they should not weigh against the theory of the origin of economic cycles in natural causes. The linking of astronomic, meteorological, agricultural, and economic causes places the whole discussion upon a rational, rather than upon an empirical, basis. There are uncertainties in respect to several links, but with the accumulation of weather data meteorologists are facing with an open mind the problem of periodicities; and with the startling discoveries in electricity and magnetism, solar physicists are advancing revolutionary views regarding the Sun's radiation, the interrelations of the planets, and the nature of the interplanetary medium.

APPENDIX

TABLE I.—ANNUAL RAINFALL IN THE UNITED STATES AS A UNIT
DEPARTURES SMOOTHED BY THE FORMULA
$$b = \tfrac{1}{4}\,(a + 2b + c)$$

Year	Professor Henry's smoothed departures		Year	Professor Henry's smoothed departures	
	Original data Inches	Corrected data Inches		Original data Inches	Corrected data Inches
1881	+0.4	+0.4	1901	—2.1	—2.1
1882	+0.2	+0.2	1902	—2.0	—2.0
1883	±0.0	±0.0	1903	—2.5	—2.5
1884	+0.4	+0.4	1904	—2.6	—2.6
1885	—0.4	—0.4	1905	—1.0	—1.0
1886	—2.7	—2.7	1906	—0.4	—0.4
1887	—3.2	—3.2	1907	—1.6	—1.6
1888	—2.1	—2.1	1908	—1.8	—1.8
1889	—2.0	—2.0	1909	—2.4	—2.4
1890	—2.4	—2.4	1910	—3.8	—3.8
1891	—1.3	—2.3	1911	—2.6	—2.6
1892	—2.5	—2.5	1912	—1.1	—1.1
1893	—3.1	—3.1	1913	—1.8	—2.3
1894	—3.5	—3.5	1914	—1.9	—1.9
1895	—3.2	—3.2	1915	—1.5	—1.5
1896	—2.1	—2.1	1916	—3.2	—2.9
1897	—1.6	—1.6	1917	—4.7	—4.7
1898	—2.1	—2.1	1918	—3.4	—3.4
1899	—2.2	—2.2	1919	—1.5	—1.5
1900	—2.0	—1.8	1920	—0.9	—1.4

CHAPTER II

GENERATING CYCLES OF PRODUCTS AND PRICES [1]

Summary

The major features of economic cycles are traceable to three primary laws: (1) the law of the generating cycle of raw materials, which is due to a non-economic cause; (2) the law of demand for raw materials, in consequence of which the generating cycle of products originates a derived cycle of prices for raw materials; and (3) the law of competitive price, according to which the prices of finished goods in an open market tend to correspond with the cost of production.

A TELLING advance was made in the theory of economic dynamics when crises were proved to be phases of economic cycles. The spectacular features of crises —panics, bankruptcies, collapse of prices, unemployment of labor, and subsequent general depression of business—had for some time attracted attention and elicited innumerable theories as to their cause. A general characteristic of these theories was the citing of detached, non-recurring events as the separate cause of each isolated crisis. A war, a failure of some conspicuous establishment, an election, or a bad harvest were among the supposed causes. With the development of the theory of cycles the well-marked stages of prosperity, crisis, decline, and depression were described and shown to be parts of a general rhythm of industry. This more ample view of the vicissitudes of business

[1] This chapter was first published, substantially in its present form, in the *Quarterly Journal of Economics*, February, 1921.

suggested that if the rhythm as a whole could be traced to a single cause, the foundation would be laid for long-range forecasting and would, perhaps, lead to the control of economic changes in the interest of the social good.

The buoyant, expectant hope which stimulated the early searchers for a single, persistent cause of cycles is shared by few recent investigators. On the contrary, there is flat denial of the existence of any marked regularity or periodicity in the phenomena; attempts at explanation by means of a few causes are regarded as obsolete; and while recognition is made of the existence of the cycle with its separate phases, there is, in many cases, a reversion to the method of alleging isolated, separate explanations for each critical point in the several phases. The present inquiry takes up the abandoned search for a single explanation of the entire rhythm and its constituent parts.

Two accomplished investigators, Professor Aftalion,[1] and Professor Bresciani-Turroni,[2] have pointed out that the average length of cycles, since 1857, has been in the neighborhood of eight years. That fact is sufficient reason for asking why cycles are, on the average, about eight years in length, and whether this loose periodicity may not have as its origin a periodically recurring cause. Professor Mitchell, in his masterly *Business Cycles*, has given another fact of critical significance, namely, the supreme importance in each phase of the cycle of the volume and prices of raw materials. In

[1] Albert Aftalion, *Les Crises périodiques de surproduction*, vol. i, p. v, vol. ii, pp. 32, 33, and *passim*.
[2] Costantino Bresciani-Turroni, *Le Variazioni cicliche dei prezzi*, p. 57.

his description of "How Prosperity Breeds a Crisis" he has made an illuminating statement which is here quoted at length. I have taken the liberty of italicizing several sentences:

". . . The cost of materials exceeds wages in every one of the leading branches of manufacture, and in a majority of cases is over twice as large. Indeed, on the average it makes practically two-thirds of the total outlay. If wares for re-sale be substituted for materials, this proportion must run far higher in wholesale stores, while in retail shops it cannot be much lower than in factories on the average and may well be considerably higher. Even the transportation companies and enterprises in the extractive industries have to buy vast quantities of current supplies. Hence an increase in the cost of materials, wares, or supplies is often an increase in the largest single item of expense, and always an increase in an important item. *The relative fluctuations in the prices of those commodities which are bought and of those which are sold are therefore of great, in many cases of decisive, importance in determining profits.*

" Concerning these relative fluctuations, our definite information consists of index-numbers for raw materials, partially manufactured products, and finished goods; also for the same commodities at wholesale and at retail. *Now this statistical evidence points to the conclusion that what must be taken as buying prices creep up on selling prices during a period of prosperity.* Of course this movement . . . threatens a reduction of profits.

" *While a difficulty of this character seems to be encountered in most branches of business it is likely to become peculiarly acute in those manufacturing industries which use animal and farm products as their leading raw materials.* For, following up a suggestion of Sombart's, we have found that these classes of products are more erratic in their price fluctuations than are the products of mines and forests. Hence an uncommonly large speculative risk must be borne, or insured against, in such branches of trade as meat packing, flour milling, cotton spinning, woollen weaving, tanning, etc. Of course this risk exists during all phases of the business cycle, but it is augmented in prosperity by the necessity of carrying larger stocks of raw materials. *The census indicates that more than three-fourths of all the 'materials purchased in the raw state' by American factories in 1900 belonged to this class which is peculiarly unstable in price.*" [1]

Now may it not be that the physical yield of the farms, which supplied more than three-fourths of all the raw materials of American factories in 1900, is itself a

---

[1] W. C. Mitchell, *Business Cycles*, pp. 481, 482. To the above statement Professor Mitchell appends the following note, p. 482, note 10.

"The sources of raw materials are given as follows:

From farms		$1,941,000,000
"	forests	119,000,000
"	mines	320,000,000
"	the sea	10,000,000
"	all sources	$2,490,000,000

Twelfth Census of the United States, Manufactures, Part I, p. cxxxv."

There is a slight error in the above value "from all sources." The aggregate sum is $2,390,000,000, and this would make the proportion contributed by the farms 81.2 per cent.

periodically varying magnitude that will produce a corresponding rhythm in the prices of raw materials and the prices of products derived therefrom? Is it not possible that this same periodicity may be of such length as to approximate the average length of cycles which has been noted by Professor Aftalion and Professor Bresciani-Turroni?

If we discover this periodicity in the yield of farm products, we shall make a distinction between generating economic cycles and derived economic cycles. Generating economic cycles will then be economic cycles which have their origin in non-economic causes and are themselves the originating source of derived economic cycles. If the varying yield of the crops has its origin in a periodic meteorological cause, it will itself be periodic and will generate periodic sequences in the whole of the dependent economic changes. If the existence of such a generating cycle is established, there will be no need, in treating the phases of economic cycles, to seek separate explanations for their existence. The phases of the generating cycles will themselves originate corresponding phases in the dependent, derived cycles.

The Correlation of Crop Yields and Crop Prices

From the point of view of the value of the product, our crops ranked, in 1919, in the following order: corn, wheat, cotton, hay, oats, potatoes. These six crops, in 1919, contributed 70.8 per cent of the value of the multitudinous crops produced by our farms. The aggregate value of all the crops produced in 1919 was, according to the estimate [1] of the Secretary of Agriculture, $15,873,000,000, and of this aggregate amount the above six products contributed $11,238,536,000. The records of the yields and prices of these six crops from 1882 give the statistical material of which use is made in the subsequent investigation.

As the American production in case of all six of these commodities is only a part of the world supply, our first inquiry will be whether, notwithstanding this fact, the domestic prices are immediately related to the domestic yield. Furthermore, as we wish to eliminate the varying factor of changing acreage, our inquiry will take the form of ascertaining whether the domestic prices of these several crops are immediately related to the respective yields per acre.

In order to secure a certain degree of comparability in the graphs, the raw figures [2] of yield and the corresponding December farm price were, for each crop, converted into index numbers in which the average yield and the average price for the years 1890–99 were taken as the respective bases. The graphs of these index numbers of yield and prices are given in Figures 4, 5, 6. In each of the six graphs of yield and the six graphs of prices the statistics show a secular trend which must be ascertained as a preliminary to the work of finding the relation between the variations in yield and the variations in prices. In each of the twelve curves the secular trend was obtained by fitting a curve of the type

$$y = a + bx + cx^2 + dx^3$$

[1] *Yearbook of the Department of Agriculture*, 1919, p. 17.

[2] The raw figures of yield per acre and December farm prices were taken from the *Yearbooks of the Department of Agriculture*.

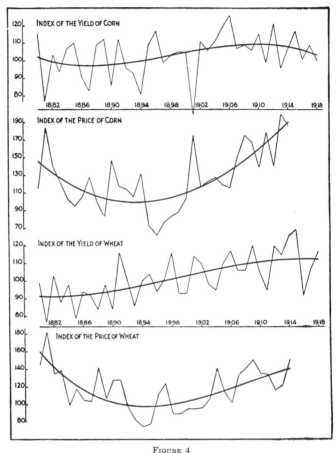

FIGURE 4

Secular trends in the index numbers of the yield and price of corn and wheat.
Corn: Yield, $y = 103.9 + .838x - .0032x^2 - .002,233x^3$, origin at 1899;
        Price, $y = 102.4 + 1.690x + .2275x^2 - .001,288x^3$, origin at 1897.
Wheat: Yield, $y = 102.1 + .952x - .0004x^2 - .001,101x^3$, origin at 1899;
        Price, $y = 99.2 + 1.057x + .1780x^2 - .005,570x^3$, origin at 1897.

to the data, and the resulting equations were found to be those that are given in the descriptions of Figures 4, 5, and 6. The origins of the equations are different in the two graphs, because the crops are taken from

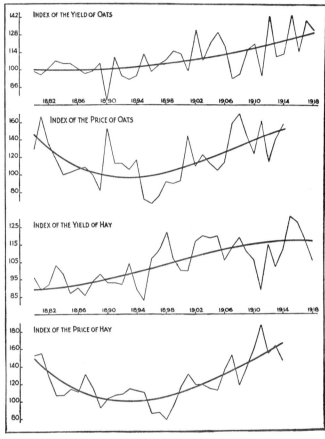

FIGURE 5

Secular trends in the index numbers of the yield and price of oats and hay.

Oats: Yield, $y = 105.7 + .805x + .0258x^2 - .000,038x^3$, origin at 1899;
Price, $y = 100.6 + 1.700x + .1692x^2 - .005,271x^3$, origin at 1897.
Hay: Yield, $y = 104.9 + 1.156x - .0049x^2 - .001,816x^3$, origin at 1899;
Price, $y = 103.1 + 1.696x + .1882x^2 - .004,042x^3$, origin at 1897.

1880 to 1918, and the prices, owing to the abnormal fluctuations during the war, only from 1880 to 1914.

The next step in the inquiry is to determine whether the percentage variations of the yields of the sev-

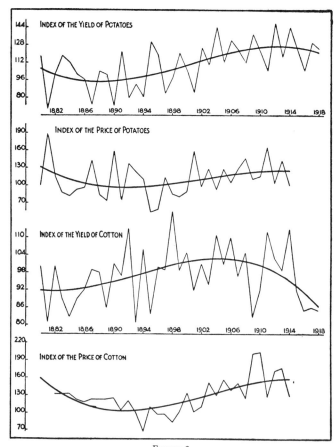

FIGURE 6

Secular trends in the index numbers of the yield and price of potatoes and cotton.
Potatoes: Yield, $y = 108.2 + 1.992x + .0179x^2 - .004,435x^3$, origin at 1899;
Price, $y = 101.6 + 1.612x + .0921x^2 - .006,101x^3$, origin at 1897.
Cotton: Yield, $y = 101.2 + .548x - .0331x^2 - .001,901x^3$, origin at 1899;
Price, $y = 111.0 + 2.688x + .1667x^2 - .009,536x^3$, origin at 1897.

eral crops from their respective secular trends are
related to the corresponding percentage variations
of prices from the respective secular trends of prices.
The method of investigation will be made clearer

by an illustration. The equation descriptive of the secular trend in the yield of corn was found to be

$$y = 103.9 + .838x - .0032x^2 - .002,233x^3$$

with origin at 1899. The graph of this equation is the smooth curve in the upper part of Figure 4. The equation descriptive of the secular trend of the December farm price of corn was found to be

$$y = 102.4 + 1.690x + .2275x^2 - .001,288x^3$$

with origin at 1897, the graph of which is also given in Figure 4. The percentage deviations from the secular trend of the actual yield per acre for the separate years from 1880 to 1914 were computed, and these percentage deviations were then correlated with the corresponding percentage deviations of the actual prices from the price secular trend. Table I in the Appendix, which refers to corn, gives an illustration of the computations. Similar calculations were made for the remaining five crops, and the coefficients of correlation between the corresponding percentage deviations, for the years 1880–1914, were computed. The resulting coefficients were these:

Corn...................................	$r = - .78$
Wheat.................................	$r = .- .23$
Cotton................................	$r = - .45$
Hay...................................	$r = - .68$
Oats..................................	$r = - .67$
Potatoes..............................	$r = - .90$

Notwithstanding the fact that the American production of these crops is only a part of the world supply, there is an inverse relation between the percentage deviations of the yield per acre of our crops and the percentage deviations of the corresponding prices.

Generating Cycles of Products

We have just established an inverse relation between the yield per acre of each of the six representative crops and their respective prices. If now we can show that the combined yield of the crops is periodic, there will be excellent reason for believing that their combined prices will be periodic and that the prices of commodities produced from farm materials will tend to show the same well-defined rhythm. Our immediate problem, therefore, is to discover whether there is a periodic cycle in the combined yield of the six representative crops.

To go forward with the work we needed to compute an index number of the combined yield of the representative crops. In treating the preceding question as to the correlation of the yield of the several crops with their respective prices, we computed, in each case, the percentage deviations of the yield per acre from the secular trend. For our present purpose of finding whether the combined yield of the six crops tends to run in cycles, the percentage deviations of the yield of the several crops for each year of the record, from 1882 to 1918, were added. The resulting figures, which are given in Table II of the Appendix, constitute our index numbers of the yield per acre of the six crops.

In the attempt to learn whether, during the interval under investigation, the yield of the crops was cyclical and periodic, the periodogram of the yield was computed and the graph was drawn. The results of the computation are given in Table III of the Appendix, and the graph appears at the top of Figure 7. The

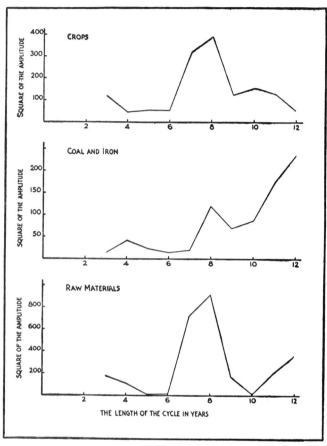

FIGURE 7

Periodograms of crops, coal and iron, and raw materials of manufacture.

periodogram shows that if there is a periodicity between three and twelve years in the data, its most probable length is in the neighborhood of eight years. When the probable cycle of eight years is computed, its maxima are found to occur, approximately, at 1882, 1890, 1898, 1906, 1914. The graph of the eight-year

cycle is given in the lower part of Figure 8. This outcome of the calculations is gratifying because of its
consonance with results that have already been obtained. Other investigations [1] have shown that there
are eight-year cycles with maxima approximately at
1882, 1890, 1898, 1906, 1914 in ,the annual rainfall of
the United States as a unit, in the annual rainfall of
the Ohio Valley, the May and June rainfall of the Dakotas,
and in the yield of wheat, oats, and barley in the Dakotas, the United States, the United Kingdom, and
France.

The Derived Cycle of Prices

An index number of the combined yield of the six
crops was devised, as we have just described, by summing the percentage deviations of the yields from their
respective secular trends. To carry the inquiry beyond
the stage that was reached in the last section an index
number of the combined prices of the six crops was constructed by summing, for each year, the percentage
deviations of the prices of the several crops from the
respective secular trends of prices. The data are given
in Table IV of the Appendix. These two index numbers—the index of the combined yield and the index of
the combined prices—supplied the material for the
next stage in the problem, namely, to ascertain the
degree of relation between the variations in the index

[1] "Forecasting the Crops of the Dakotas," *Political Science Quarterly*,
June, 1919, pp. 228, 229   "Crop Cycles in the United Kingdom and
in the United States," *Journal of the Royal Statistical Society*, May, 1919.
"Crop Cycles in the United Kingdom and in France," *ibid.*, May, 1920.
"An Eight-Year Rainfall Cycle," *Monthly Weather Review*, July, 1922.

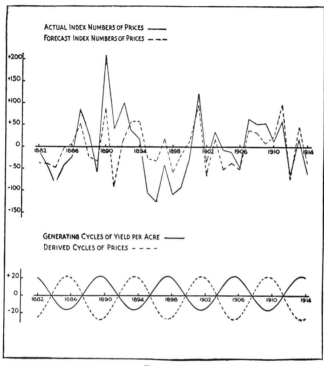

FIGURE 8

Upper part: Actual index numbers of prices of the six representative crops and
the index numbers of prices forecast from the index numbers of
the yield per acre by means of the formula
$$y = -1.295x - .02.$$
Lower part: Generating cycles of the yield per acre of the crops,
$$y = 1.6 + 20.0 \sin (45°t + 109°), \text{ origin at } 1882;$$
Derived cycles of prices of the crops computed from the generating
cycles of yield by means of the formula,
$$y = -1.295x - .02.$$

of the combined yield and the index of the combined
prices.

The coefficient of correlation between these two
variables is $r = -.69$, and the equation expressing
their relation is

$$y = -1.295x - .02$$

where x = the index of the yield and y = the index of prices. This close relation indicates that the eight-year cycle in the yield per acre of the crops tends to generate an eight-year cycle in the prices of the products. Figure 8 shows, in its upper half, the course of the index number of actual prices and the course of the theoretical index when

$$y = -1.295x - .02$$

is used as a forecasting formula. The lower half of Figure 8 shows the generating eight-year cycle in the yield per acre of the crops and the derived eight-year cycle in the prices of the crops. The equation of the generating cycle of products was obtained in the preceding section. The derived cycle of prices was computed from the generating cycle of products by means of the formula connecting the variations of the combined yield with the variations of the combined prices.

$$y = -1.295x - .02$$

Cycles in the Products of Mines

We have noted that according to the census of 1900, the values of raw materials used in manufactures were as follows: from farms, $1,941,000,000; from forests, $119,000,000; from mines $320,000,000; from the sea, $10,000,000. Of the aggregate value of these materials, 81.2 per cent was supplied by the farms; 5.0 per cent by the forests; 13.4 per cent by the mines; and 0.4 per cent by the sea. We have already shown that the yield of the leading farm crops moves in well-defined cycles which generate corresponding cycles of agricultural prices. The leading crops upon which the computation was based supplied 70 per cent of the total value of American crops in 1919 and are therefore sufficiently representative of the yield and prices of farm products. Next to the farms, according to the above figures, the mines furnish the most important source of materials for manufactures. The farms and the mines together supplied, in 1900, 94.6 per cent of the value of the raw materials used in American factories. Does the production of minerals move in cycles?

The most important minerals for the use of manufactures and transportation are coal and iron, and in our further inquiry these two minerals will be regarded as being representative of the products of the mines just as the six crops—corn, wheat, oats, hay, cotton, and potatoes—were treated as being representative of the products of the farm.

In preparing the statistics of the production of coal and pig iron with a view to ascertaining whether there is any periodicity in their production, the procedure was similar to that which was followed in the case of the yield of the crops. The raw figures [1] of production were first reduced to index numbers in which the mean production for 1890–99 was placed as equal to 100. The graphs of the index numbers of production are given in Figure 9. Because of the enormous and irregular increase in the production of both coal and iron in the interval under investigation, 1881–1913, the description of the secular trends by means of single equations requires the use of a slightly more complex curve than

---

[1] The figures were taken from the *Statistical Abstract of the United States*, 1915, pp. 689, 690.

the one employed in the treatment of the yield and prices of farm products. In the latter case a parabola of the type

$$y = a + bx + cx^2 + dx^3$$

was found to give a satisfactory fit. But in the description of the secular trends in the production of coal and iron an additional term was added to the above equation, and a parabola of the fourth order

$$y = a + bx + cx^2 + dx^3 + ex^4$$

was fitted to the data. The graphs in Figure 9 show the secular trend of both coal and iron, and the corresponding equations are given in the legend descriptive of Figure 9.

After the secular trend of coal and the secular trend of iron were ascertained, the percentage deviations of the production of each commodity in the years from 1882–1913 were computed. These percentage deviations were then combined into an index number of the deviations in the production of coal and iron by summing the percentage deviations for each year. The data are given in Table V of the Appendix. Because of the abnormal demand for coal and iron during the war the figures were not extended beyond 1913.

If now the index numbers of the deviations in the production of coal and iron from 1882 to 1913 are scrutinized with a view to discovering periodicities, we find that the periodogram takes the shape that is pictured in the second curve in Figure 7. The data are given in Table III of the Appendix.

It is obvious from the periodogram that if there are real cycles in the production of coal and iron, the most

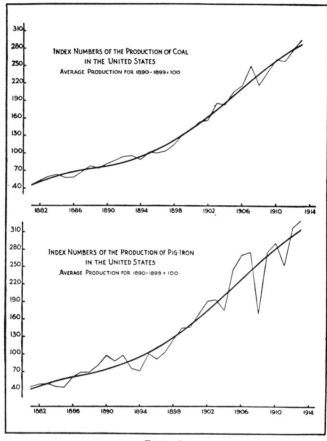

Figure 9

Secular trends in the index numbers of the production of coal and pig iron in the
    United States.
    Coal: $y = 114.1 + 7.777x + .4131x^2 - .000,751x^3 - .000,8141x^4$,   origin   at
        1897;
    Pig Iron: $y = 119.4 + 9.199x + .4110x^2 - .002,561x^3 - .000,7239x^4$,   origin   at
        1897.

probable are in the neighborhood of eight and eleven or
twelve years in length, but in the present paper we shall
confine the discussion to the eight-year cycle. When

the equation to the eight-year cycle is computed, the maxima are found to occur approximately at 1882, 1890, 1898, 1906, 1914. And if the eight-year cycle in the production of coal and iron is graphed and compared with the graph of the eight-year cycle in the yield of the crops, the coal and iron curve is found to lag about three-tenths of a year behind the curve for the crop yield. The graphs are given at the top of Figure 10.

Cycles in the Production of the Raw Materials of Manufacture

The production of the farms and the mines taken separately tends to run in eight-year cycles, the cycles of the raw materials from the mines inclining to lag a few months behind the cycles in the yield of the crops. The farms and the mines together supplied, in 1900, 95 per cent of the raw materials of American factories, and, consequently, their joint production affords both an adequate measure of the changes in the volume of raw materials and a valuable index of the changes in the physical volume of trade. Is there any regularity in the joint production of the farms and the mines?

In the same manner in which we constructed an index number of the yield of the crops and an index number of the production of coal and iron, we made an index number of the raw materials of manufacture. The percentage deviations of the yield of the crops and the percentage deviations of the production of coal and iron were summed, and the aggregate percentage deviations were regarded as the index numbers of the production of raw materials. The data are given in Tables II and V of the Appendix.

When the index numbers of raw materials from 1882 to 1913 were scrutinized for the purpose of discovering periodicities, it was found that the periodogram took the shape of the bottom curve in Figure 7 showing that

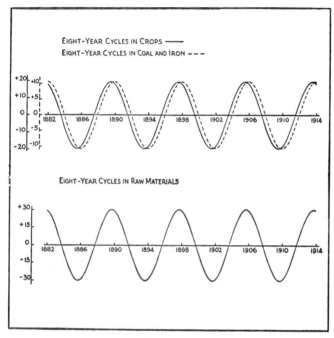

FIGURE 10

Cycles in the yield of the crops, the production of coal and iron, and the production of the raw materials of manufacture.

Crops: $y = 20.0 \sin (45°t + 109°)$, origin at 1882;
Coal and Iron: $y = 11.0 \sin (45°t + 93°)$, origin at 1882;
Raw Materials: $y = 30.3 \sin (45°t + 103°)$, origin at 1882.

if there is a cycle in the production of raw materials of manufacture in the United States, its probable length is about eight years. The computations referring to the periodogram are given in Table III of the Appendix. If the eight-year cycle in the production of the raw materials of manufacture is computed, its maxima will occur, approximately, at 1882, 1890, 1898, 1906, 1914, and the graph of the cycle will run in the manner described in the bottom curve of Figure 10.

There are two observations with regard to the theory of economic cycles that need to be emphasized by frequent repetition. The first was made by Professor Aftalion, the second by Rodbertus.

After estimating the average length of cycles since 1857 at approximately eight years, Professor Aftalion stated that the essential problem in the theory of economic cycles is to discover the cause of the rhythm. "L'observation du rythme de la production générale fait . . . seulement comprendre la *survenance* d'une hausse, puis d'une baisse générale des prix, l'existence d'un rythme. Elle ne nous donne pas l'explication de la *durée* de cette hausse ni de cette baisse, de la durée des phases du rythme." [1]

In one of the briefer essays of Rodbertus, "Physiokratie und Anthropokratie," [2] the initiator of the socialist theory of business cycles stresses the importance of discovering the natural cause of the economic rhythm in order that society may set about adjusting itself in the light of the acquired knowledge. He draws the distinction between the rule of nature—Physiokratie— and the rule of man—Anthropokratie. Quesnay and Adam Smith and their followers, according to Rodbertus, regarded the problems of social science primarily

[1] Albert Aftalion, *Les Crises périodiques de surproduction*, vol. ii, pp. 41, 42.

[2] Rodbertus-Jagetzow, *Briefe und Socialpolitische Aufsätze*.

from the point of view of physical science and were led
to the maxim *"laissez aller et laissez passer; le monde va
de lui-même."* By contrast Rodbertus would empha-
size the great possibilities of social progress through the
intervention of the state and the utilization of natural
laws for social purposes. With regard to the specific
problem of economic cycles, the natural law and cause
of the rhythm must be discovered and then utilized by
society for its own ends. "Sich im Staatsleben Natur-
gesetzen zu unterwerfen, heisst, sich des 'Göttlichen' im
Menschen begeben, heisst, von socialen Organismen,
muthwillig in Krankheit und Tod gehen.

> Nach ewigen, eh'rnen
> Grossen Gesetzen
> Müssen wir Alle
> Uns'res Daseins
> Kreise vollenden.
> Nur allein der Mensch
> Vermag das Unmögliche;
> Er unterscheidet,
> Wählet und richtet;
>
> . . . .
> Er allein darf
>
> . . . .
> Alles Irrende, Schweifende
> Nützlich verbinden."
>
> Goethe: *Das Göttliche.*

APPENDIX

TABLE I.—Correlation of the Percentage Deviations of the Price of Corn with the Percentage Deviations of the Yield per Acre of Corn

Year	Index number of the yield of corn	General trend of the yield of corn	Percentage deviation from the trend	Index number of the price of corn	General trend of the price of corn	Percentage deviation from the trend
1880	114	102	+11.8	115	146	−21.2
1881	77	101	−23.8	184	139	+32.4
1882	102	100	+ 2.0	141	133	+ 6.0
1883	94	99	− 5.1	123	127	− 3.1
1884	107	98	+ 9.2	103	122	−15.6
1885	110	98	+12.2	95	117	−18.8
1886	91	97	− 6.2	106	113	− 6.2
1887	83	97	−14.4	129	110	+17.3
1888	109	97	+12.4	99	107	− 7.5
1889	112	97	+15.5	82	104	−21.2
1890	86	98	−12.2	147	102	+44.1
1891	112	98	+14.3	118	101	+16.8
1892	96	99	− 3.0	114	100	+14.0
1893	93	99	− 6.1	106	99	+ 7.1
1894	80	100	−20.0	132	99	+33.3
1895	109	101	+ 7.9	73	100	−27.0
1896	117	101	+15.8	62	101	−38.6
1897	99	102	− 2.9	76	102	−25.5
1898	103	103	0.0	83	104	−20.2
1899	105	104	+ 1.0	88	107	−17.8
1900	105	105	0.0	103	109	− 5.5
1901	69	106	−34.9	175	113	+54.9
1902	111	106	+ 4.7	117	116	+ 0.9
1903	106	107	− 0.9	123	120	+ 2.5
1904	111	108	+ 2.8	128	125	+ 2.4
1905	120	108	+11.1	119	130	− 8.5
1906	126	109	+15.6	116	135	−14.1
1907	108	109	− 0.9	150	141	+ 6.4
1908	109	110	− 0.9	176	147	+19.7
1909	106	110	− 3.6	168	153	+ 9.8
1910	115	110	+ 4.5	139	160	−13.1
1911	99	110	−10.0	179	167	+ 7.2
1912	121	109	+11.0	141	175	−19.4
1913	96	109	−11.9	200	182	+ 9.1
1914	107	108	− 0.9	187	191	− 2.1

TABLE II.—INDEX NUMBERS OF THE YIELD PER ACRE OF SIX CROPS

Year	Percentage deviations from the respective trends of the •index numbers of yield per acre						Combined index number
	Corn	Wheat	Oats	Potatoes	Hay	Cotton	
1882	+ 2.4	+12.9	+ 1.1	+ 1.0	+ 2.9	+ 8.7	+29.0
1883	− 4.7	− 3.7	+ 7.7	+19.2	+14.6	− 3.3	+29.8
1884	+ 9.2	+ 7.8	+ 5.0	+15.5	+ 8.8	− 9.8	+36.5
1885	+12.5	−14.1	+ 5.7	+ 5.2	− 3.8	− 3.3	+ 2.2
1886	− 6.3	+ 2.0	+ 1.1	+ 1.1	− 2.0	− 1.1	− 5.2
1887	−14.1	− 0.9	− 2.9	−22.1	− 7.0	+ 6.4	−40.6
1888	+12.1	− 9.6	− 0.8	+10.6	+ 1.4	+ 4.3	+18.0
1889	+15.0	+ 4.4	+ 4.3	+ 6.3	+ 4.7	− 8.5	+26.2
1890	−12.1	−10.8	−25.0	−23.2	− 2.1	+ 6.3	−66.9
1891	+14.2	+22.0	+ 9.4	+27.1	− 2.9	+ 1.0	+70.8
1892	− 2.7	+ 5.9	− 8.1	−17.5	− 4.9	+17.7	− 9.6
1893	− 5.8	−10.6	−12.3	− 6.1	+ 6.0	−16.5	−45.3
1894	−19.4	+ 2.6	− 8.6	−18.2	−10.1	+ 8.2	−45.5
1895	+ 8.1	+ 5.5	+ 9.8	+29.7	−17.4	−15.2	+20.5
1896	+15.4	− 5.4	− 5.2	+15.5	+ 5.5	+ 1.0	+26.8
1897	− 3.3	+ 1.3	− 0.4	−19.2	+ 8.9	− 1.0	−13.7
1898	− 0.2	+14.5	+ 3.3	− 7.5	+16.8	+17.8	+44.7
1899	+ 1.1	− 8.7	+ 9.1	+12.0	+ 2.0	− 2.0	+13.5
1900	+ 0.3	− 9.6	+ 6.1	− 4.5	− 5.7	+ 2.9	−10.5
1901	−34.4	+ 9.2	− 8.3	−24.1	− 6.7	− 9.8	−74.1
1902	+ 4.6	+ 4.7	+21.6	+ 9.6	+ 8.2	− 1.1	+47.6
1903	− 1.2	− 7.7	− 0.8	− 5.2	+10.0	− 8.7	−13.6
1904	+ 3.3	−11.2	+11.0	+22.0	+ 7.5	+ 7.8	+40.4
1905	+10.3	+ 2.0	+16.5	− 5.8	+ 8.0	− 1.9	+29.1
1906	+15.4	+ 8.3	+ 5.8	+ 9.0	− 6.1	+ 6.8	+39.2
1907	− 1.6	− 2.8	−20.5	+ 0.8	+ 0.1	− 4.9	−28.9
1908	− 0.8	− 3.5	−17.0	− 9.7	+ 4.1	+ 2.9	−24.0
1909	− 3.6	+ 8.3	− 0.6	+10.4	− 3.4	−17.8	− 6.7
1910	+ 4.6	− 5.1	+ 2.6	− 3.2	− 8.0	− 8.9	−18.0
1911	− 9.5	−15.1	−21.8	−17.3	−23.2	+12.0	−74.9
1912	+10.9	+ 7.6	+18.5	+16.5	− 1.5	+ 5.1	+57.1
1913	−11.9	+ 2.6	− 8.5	− 7.1	−12.4	+ 2.1	−35.2
1914	− 1.0	+11.7	− 8.1	+13.4	− 4.7	+18.9	+30.2
1915	+ 8.9	+14.3	+15.4	− 0.8	+11.9	− 2.1	+47.6
1916	− 4.8	−18.6	− 9.2	−16.0	+ 9.2	− 6.6	−46.0
1917	+ 4.0	− 5.2	+ 8.9	+ 5.6	+ 0.7	− 3.4	+10.6
1918	− 3.7	+ 4.4	+ 1.6	+ 2.5	− 9.2	− 2.3	− 6.7

TABLE III.—Periodograms of the Index Numbers of the Yield
per Acre of the Crops, the Production of Coal and Iron,
and the Production of the Raw Materials of Manufacture

Length of the cycle (years)	Square of the amplitude		
	Crops	Coal and iron	Raw materials
3	148.65	14.12	182.17
4	41.15	42.37	110.64
5	67.18	24.41	5.92
6	65.20	13.13	11.45
7	319.21	21.03	725.32
8	401.24	120.41	919.26
9	123.92	70.41	170.32
10	155.16	87.49	16.42
11	129.95	176.26	211.03
12	54.31	237.70	368.68

TABLE IV.—INDEX NUMBERS OF THE DECEMBER FARM PRICES OF
SIX CROPS

Year	Percentage deviations from the respective trends of the index numbers of the December farm prices						Combined index number
	Corn	Wheat	Oats	Potatoes	Hay	Cotton	
1882	+ 6.0	− 4.9	+ 3.1	− 2.5	− 4.5	− 5.7	− 8.5
1883	− 3.1	+ 3.0	− 4.8	−22.8	−15.7	0.0	− 43.4
1884	−15.6	−22.7	−16.0	−25.5	−12.3	+ 6.4	− 85.7
1885	−18.8	− 3.3	− 9.6	−12.3	− 2.6	+ 2.5	− 44.1
1886	− 6.2	−10.3	− 1.8	− 5.8	− 1.8	+ 2.6	− 23.3
1887	+17.3	− 7.1	+ 2.8	+40.6	+20.2	+11.8	+ 85.6
1888	− 7.5	+31.5	− 2.9	−15.2	+ 8.5	+14.9	+ 29.3
1889	−21.2	+ 1.9	−18.8	−24.5	−11.5	+17.1	− 57.0
1890	+44.1	+25.5	+54.5	+62.9	+ 1.0	+20.1	+208.1
1891	+16.8	+26.7	+15.3	−23.7	+ 6.0	+ 1.0	+ 42.1
1892	+14.0	− 4.0	+16.5	+41.2	+ 8.0	+16.5	+ 92.2
1893	+ 7.1	−16.3	+ 9.3	+26.8	+14.0	− 2.9	+ 38.0
1894	+33.3	−23.5	+20.6	+13.3	+12.0	−36.2	+ 19.5
1895	−27.0	−20.4	+26.5	−44.4	+ 9.0	+ 3.8	−105.5
1896	−38.6	+13.3	−32.3	−41.0	−15.7	−11.0	−125.3
1897	−25.5	+25.3	−24.7	+11.8	−15.5	−12.6	− 41.2
1898	−20.2	−11.0	− 9.8	−16.5	−24.8	−27.2	−109.5
1899	−17.8	−12.7	−14.3	−22.9	−11.2	−13.7	− 92.6
1900	− 5.5	− 8.7	−13.1	−15.9	+ 6.4	+10.8	− 26.0
1901	+54.9	−10.4	+30.9	+45.9	+15.9	−18.5	+118.7
1902	+ 0.9	−11.1	− 2.7	−11.7	+ 2.6	−13.4	− 35.4
1903	+ 2.5	− 4.5	+ 6.0	+13.3	0.0	+16.0	+ 33.3
1904	+ 2.4	+24.8	− 5.0	−18.3	− 7.3	− 3.7	− 7.1
1905	− 8.5	− 1.7	−13.9	+ 9.4	−11.8	+13.8	− 12.7
1906	−14.1	−14.3	− 9.5	−10.9	+ 3.8	− 2.1	− 47.1
1907	+ 6.4	+ 9.8	+23.3	+ 5.8	+13.3	+ 4.1	+ 62.7
1908	+19.7	+13.6	+27.8	+20.5	−15.1	−14.9	+ 51.6
1909	+ 9.8	+18.0	+ 6.6	− 9.7	− 4.2	+33.1	+ 53.6
1910	−13.1	+ 3.8	−11.4	− 7.2	+ 7.4	+33.3	+ 12.8
1911	+ 7.2	0.0	+13.3	+32.8	+22.9	−17.4	+ 58.8
1912	−19.4	−14.7	−21.2	−16.7	− 1.3	+ 9.6	− 63.7
1913	+ 9.9	−12.2	− 6.0	+13.5	+ 0.6	+12.0	+ 17.8
1914	− 2.1	+ 7.1	+ 3.9	−19.8	−12.0	−37.3	− 60.2

TABLE V.—INDEX NUMBERS OF COAL AND PIG IRON

| Year | Percentage deviations from secular trend | | Combined index numbers |
	Coal	Iron	
1882	+ 1.9	+ 6.5	+ 8.4
1883	+ 5.3	− 2.0	+ 3.3
1884	+ 3.3	−18.5	−15.2
1885	−10.8	−25.9	−36.7
1886	−13.2	0.0	−13.2
1887	− 2.9	+ 7.8	+ 4.9
1888	+ 6.8	+ 3.0	+ 9.8
1889	− 1.3	+15.7	+14.4
1890	+ 5.1	+32.4	+37.5
1891	+ 8.6	+11.4	+20.0
1892	+10.6	+16.7	+27.3
1893	+ 6.7	−14.6	− 7.9
1894	− 5.3	−26.0	−31.3
1895	+ 1.0	− 1.9	− 0.9
1896	− 6.5	−17.1	−23.6
1897	− 8.8	−13.4	−22.2
1898	− 5.7	− 2.3	− 8.0
1899	+ 0.8	+ 4.3	+ 5.1
1900	0.0	− 2.7	− 2.7
1901	+ 0.7	+ 4.9	+ 5.6
1902	− 3.7	+ 9.1	+ 5.4
1903	+ 6.9	+ 2.7	+ 9.6
1904	− 2.1	−12.4	−14.5
1905	+ 3.0	+14.4	+17.4
1906	+ 1.9	+18.3	+20.2
1907	+11.6	+13.6	+25.2
1908	− 8.4	−33.6	−42.0
1909	− 3.6	+ 2.2	− 1.4
1910	+ 0.8	+ 3.5	+ 4.3
1911	− 4.4	−13.9	−18.3
1912	− 0.4	+ 4.3	+ 3.9
1913	+ 3.1	+ 5.4	+ 8.5

CHAPTER III

GENERATING CYCLES REFLECTED IN A CENTURY OF PRICES [1]

Summary

Cycles of approximately eight years in the yield per acre of British crops have probably recurred in a continuous series during the last one hundred and sixty years. In consequence of the law of demand, these crop cycles have generated corresponding cycles in the prices of food and of organic raw materials. In conformity with the law of competitive price, the cycles in the prices of food and of raw materials should have been followed by corresponding cycles in the prices of manufactured commodities. As a matter of fact, the analysis of Sauerbeck's index numbers of general wholesale prices reveals real cycles of approximately eight years in which the originating, generating crop cycles are reflected throughout the century for which the Sauerbeck index numbers have been computed.

The principal results of the investigation appear in the graphs of Figures 15 and 16.

In the preceding chapter I drew a distinction between generating economic cycles and derived economic cycles. Generating economic cycles were described as economic cycles that have their origin in non-economic causes and become the originating source of derived economic cycles. A careful scrutiny of American agricultural statistics revealed the existence of an eight-year generating cycle in the yield per acre of the leading American crops, and this generating cycle of products

---

[1] This chapter was first published, substantially in its present from, in the *Quarterly Journal of Economics*, August, 1921.

was found to originate a derived cycle of agricultural prices. American manufactures, according to the census of 1900, obtained about 80 per cent of their raw materials from the farms, and as the prices of manufactured commodities tend to adjust themselves to the cost of production, it was argued that the eight-year cycles in the prices of farm products tended to induce derivative cycles in the prices of manufactured commodities. The major features of economic cycles were regarded as being traceable to three primary laws:

(1) the law of the generating cycle of raw materials, which is due to a non-economic cause;

(2) the law of demand for raw materials, in consequence of which the generating cycle of products originates a derived cycle of prices for raw materials; and

(3) the law of competitive price, according to which prices of finished goods in an open market tend to correspond with the cost of production.

The inquiry is now carried a stage further. An analysis is made of the history of prices in Great Britain, for a century, and the results are considered with reference to their dependence upon generating agricultural cycles and with regard to their bearing upon the economic theory of cycles.

Data and Method

The data for the first part of the investigation are the Sauerbeck index numbers of general wholesale prices for the interval between the Napoleonic wars and the Great War. This record from 1818 to 1913, which

is a summary description of economic history during a
century of unparalleled development between two
world-wide catastrophes, supplies unique material for
an inductive quest of economic regularities.

The method used in the inquiry is Fourier's Theorem
as it has been developed for statistical purposes by
Professor Schuster and Professor Turner.

The Savilian Professor of Astronomy at Oxford,
Professor Turner, has said that "apart from the planetary motions periodicities in nature are seldom clear-
cut." [1] As we shall attempt to establish certain
economic cycles and to trace their cause to periodicities
in nature, the part of wisdom would seem to be to
profit by the experience of natural scientists who have
dealt with the problem of isolating natural periodicities.
It is well known that Fourier's celebrated theorem

$$y = A_0 + a_1 \cos kt + a_2 \cos 2kt + \ldots$$
$$+ b_1 \sin kt + b_2 \sin 2kt + \ldots$$

if carried out to a sufficient number of terms will repro-
duce almost any type of graph. This equation may be
expressed also in the form

$$y = A_0 + A_1 \sin (kt + e_1) + A_2 \sin (2kt + e_2) + \ldots$$

When the parameters of this equation are determined
from statistical data the question arises as to the significance of the several terms in the Fourier series. Do
the successive terms in the sine series correspond to
real periodicities in nature, or are they merely formal
terms the summation of which will give the observed

[1] H. H. Turner, *Tables for Facilitating the Use of Harmonic Analysis*,
p. 44.

values of the original data?   If, for example, a high
value were obtained for one of the A-coefficients in the
sine series, what warrant would there be for assuming
that the particular sine term of which the given A was
the coefficient would be significant of a real recurring
periodicity?

This problem was considered by Professor Schuster
in his theory of the periodogram.[1] According to Professor Schuster, "the periodogram may be said to put the
statistical material in a form in which it may be most
readily discussed, but there may be always cases in
which the interpretation is difficult. . . . I do not, of
course, claim to have first introduced the application
of Fourier's Theorem to the discovery of hidden
periodicities. . . . The process is sufficiently obvious to
have been frequently introduced, but it has generally
been assumed that each maximum in the amplitude of a
harmonic term corresponded to a true periodicity.
What distinguishes the method which I am endeavour-
ing to introduce from that of others, is the discussion
of the natural variability of the Fourier coefficients
according to the theory of probability, independently
of any periodic cause which may have influenced the
phenomenon." [2]

[1] The fundamental memoirs of Professor Schuster are:

"On the Investigation of Hidden Periodicities with Application to a
Supposed 26 Day Period of Meteorological Phenomena," *Terrestrial
Magnetism*, for March, 1898; "The Periodogram of Magnetic Declination as Obtained from the Records of the Greenwich Observatory during
the Years 1871–1895," *Cambridge Philosophical Society Transactions*,
vol. 18, 1899; "On the Periodicity of Sunspots," *Philosophical Transactions of the Royal Society of London*, A, vol. 206, 1906.

[2] "On the Periodicities of Sunspots," *Philosophical Transactions*, A,
vol. 206, pp. 71, 72.

The first step in the Schuster method of isolating true periodicities by the method of the periodogram consists in arranging the data of the statistical series into groups of different lengths and then computing the values of the coefficients of the sine terms appropriate to the different groups. The required lengths and closeness of the groups are discussed [1] by Professor Schuster, and he further shows how the probability of the reality of any assumed cycle is dependent upon the magnitude of the coefficient of its corresponding harmonic in the periodogram. In brief, the probability of the reality of an assumed cycle is shown to be dependent upon the relative size of A^2 where A is the coefficient of the sine term descriptive of the assumed cycle.

Professor Turner's method, which he has called the method of Fourier Sequence,[2] is based upon Professor Schuster's method of the periodogram. The device may be illustrated by the problem in connection with which the method of Fourier Sequence was developed. In 1913, when Professor Turner published his essays, a fairly good record of sunspots existed for a period of 156 years. His problem was to determine whether there

[1] See particularly "On the Periodicities of Sunspots," *Philosophical Transactions*, A, vol. 206, p. 71.

[2] The fundamental memoirs of Professor Turner are "On the Harmonic Analysis of Wolf's Sun-spot Numbers, With Special Reference to Mr. Kimura's Paper," *Monthly Notices of the Royal Astronomical Society*, May, 1913; "On the Expression of Sunspot Periodicity as a Fourier Sequence, and on the General Use of a Fourier Sequence in Similar Problems," *ibid.*, 1913 (Supplement); "Further Remarks on the Expression of Sun-spot Periodicity as a Fourier Sequence," *ibid.*, November, 1913.

was ground for believing that there were real periodicities in the sunspot data, and if so, to ascertain their approximate lengths. The same problem had been considered by Professor Schuster with the aid of the method of the periodogram, but, according to Professor Turner, the Schuster method was needlessly complex, involving an unnecessary amount of computation. An adequate solution was thought to be obtained if a Fourier series were computed for the whole series of data, and the several terms of the series were investigated more in detail according as the magnitudes and signs of the coefficients of the several terms indicated the possible presence of a real cycle. In order to carry out this idea, Professor Turner computed for the 156 years of sunspot data the harmonics for the periods of the following number of years: 156, 156/2, 156/3 . . . 156/54. The principal advantage claimed by Professor Turner for the method of Fourier Sequence is this: The development of the Fourier Sequence is

(1) *Necessary.*—"Since each term of the Fourier Sequence is independent of every other, it cannot be inferred from any other. Hence we must at least calculate all these terms." [1]

(2) *Sufficient.*—"If we desire to know to what extent any periodicity intermediate between two of those directly tabulated is represented in the observations . . . we are able to deduce this information from the sequence." [2]

[1] "On the Expression of Sun-spot Periodicity as a Fourier Sequence," *Monthly Notices of the Royal Astronomical Society*, 1913, p. 715.

[2] *Ibid.*, p. 715.

An Analysis of a Century of Prices

As a preliminary step our investigation will follow the method of Professor Turner in the analysis of Sauerbeck's index numbers of general wholesale prices.

Sauerbeck's index numbers of general wholesale prices from 1818 to 1913 are recorded in Table I of the Appendix and are graphed in Figure 11. The graph shows quite clearly that the mean value of the items in the early part of the series is higher than the mean value during the latter part, and we are, therefore, confronted with the question as to what shall be done about the secular trend of the figures. Any hypothesis that might be made as to the type of curve to represent the secular trend would, to a degree, be an arbitrary hypothesis, and my decision has been to make no supposition as to the secular trend, but to proceed with the computation of the Fourier terms from the crude index numbers. In support of this decision these two considerations are offered:

1. It is known that each term of a Fourier sequence is independent of the other terms, and there is, therefore, a probability that when a Fourier series is fitted to the statistical data covering a considerable length of time, the early terms of the series will make an allowance for the secular trend which will be independent of the later terms.[1] Figures 11, 12, 13, 14 show the reasonable-

---

[1] Cf. Schuster, "The Periodogram of Magnetic Declination," p. 113. "Table . . . clearly shows the effects of secular variation, and we must consider in how far it is necessary to take any notice of this variation. If our observations extended over an indefinite time, Fourier's analysis would itself perform all that is required, and each period would be totally independent of all others."

ness of this assumption. An ample description of these graphs will be given later on.

2. The authority of Professor Schuster is against the early elimination of the secular trend before the Fourier terms are computed: "Very considerable labor has sometimes been spent in eliminating secular variations and other known periodicities before the hidden periodicities are searched for. We may reasonably ask the question, what object is thereby gained? It is one of the great advantages of Fourier's analysis that each of its terms is independent of the others; and if we wish to determine any particular coefficient it is unnecessary to begin by eliminating the others. The analysis itself performs that process in the best possible way, if the coefficients are obtained by arithmetical calculations. . . . The general rule may be given, that it is the best to eliminate as few variations as possible, and to carry out the elimination at as late a stage of the computation as possible." [1]

For these reasons we have computed the Fourier terms directly from the index numbers in the raw state. The results of the computation are given in Table II of the Appendix. The headings of the table will be understood from an examination of Fourier's series when it is expressed in the following two forms:

$$(1) \quad y = A_0 + a_1 \cos kt + a_2 \cos 2kt + \ldots$$
$$+ b_1 \sin kt + b_2 \sin 2kt + \ldots$$
$$(2) \quad y = A_0 + A_1 \sin (kt + e_1) + A_2 \sin (2kt + e_2) + \ldots$$

The amplitudes of the terms in (2)—the A-coefficients—are obtained from the corresponding coeffi-

---

[1] "On the Investigation of Hidden Periodicities," p. 34. Cf. also p. 38.

cients in (1) by means of the formula $A = \sqrt{a^2+b^2}$. A_0 is equal to the mean value of the 96 index numbers. The lengths of the periods in the second column of Table II are obtained by dividing 96, which is the number of years of observations recorded in the Sauerbeck index numbers, by the consecutive integers that are given in the first column. The constant k in the formulae (1) and (2), which does not appear in Table II, is equal to $\dfrac{360°}{96} = 3° \ 45'$. The constants e in (2) do not occur in Table II, but their values may be obtained from the corresponding values of a and b in (1) by the relation $\tan e = \dfrac{a}{b}$.

We shall now consider the conclusions that may be drawn from the data of Table II and we shall begin with the last column which gives the values of A^2. If we let the eye run down the last column, it will note that at four places the values of A^2 assume special importance— for the periods of 96 years, 48 years, 24 to 16 years, and 8.7 to 7.4 years. A moment ago when the question of eliminating the secular trend was under consideration, the decision was reached to permit the early terms of the Fourier series to provide for the secular trend rather than to adjust the raw figures of the observation according to a more or less arbitrary assumption as to the type of curve which might be appropriate to represent the trend. It now seems reasonable to conclude that the large values of A^2 at 96 years and 48 years, and possibly those between 24 and 16 years, are caused by the general trend of the figures. Inasmuch as the first of these covers the whole range of the observations and the second, one-half of the range, one would certainly not be justified in holding that they represent real recurrent cycles. Figures 11 and 12 depict these two Fourier constituents of the price curve. Figure 11 also shows the curve that is obtained by combining the mean of the Sauerbeck index numbers with the 96-year Fourier constituent. Likewise Figure 12 gives the compound curve made up of the mean of the Sauerbeck index numbers and the 96-year and 48-year Fourier constituents.

With two of the four important values of A^2 in Table II accounted for, the possibility of real cycles in the 96-years record is limited to the remaining two epochs between 24 and 16 years and between 8.7 and 7.4 years. The mean of the limiting values of the latter period is $\dfrac{8.7 + 7.4}{2} = 8.0$ years, and the limits of the other period are respectively twice and three times this mean value. The value of A^2 in Table II corresponding to a period of exactly 8 years is small, but if the computation had been confined to the interval 1857–1913 its value would have been 7.95.

Thus far the argument as to the existence of real periods has been based upon the size of A^2 which is the criterion used by Professor Schuster. An additional criterion has been offered by Professor Turner. In his fundamental memoir [1] he has pointed out that when a striking periodicity is present, there is a tendency for the signs of a and b to change between consecutive

[1] H. H. Turner, "On the Expression of Sun-spot Periodicity as a Fourier Sequence," *Monthly Notices of the Royal Astronomical Society*, 1913, p. 716. Cf. also, pp. 722, 723.

Fourier constituents. Table II shows that not only are the values of A^2 large for the period between 24 and 16 years, and for the period between 8.7 and 7.4 years, but that in both instances there is a change of sign in either a or b.

Considering that in a record of 96 years a possible cycle of about 16 years could occur six times and one of about 8 years could occur twelve times, this analysis of a century of prices seems to warrant the conclusion that there may be a real cycle of prices between 16 and 24 years in length, and that there is a large probability of the existence of a real cycle in the neighborhood of 8 years. As the argument proceeds we shall have strong additional reason for believing that the indicated eight-year cycle in the Sauerbeck index numbers of wholesale prices is a real cycle with an assignable cause. Certainly the Fourier analysis indicates that if there is a real cycle in the 96 years of the Sauerbeck observations, its most probable value is in the neighborhood of eight years.

In order to isolate and exhibit the cycles of approximately eight years the graphs of Figures 13, 14, 15 have been computed and drawn. Figure 13 shows the Fourier constituent of 19.2 years—which, according to Table II, is one of the most important constituents—and the compound curve that results from combining the mean of the Sauerbeck observations with the Fourier constituents of 96, 48, and 19.2 years. Figure 14 depicts the 16-year Fourier constituent and the compound curve made up of the mean value of the Sauerbeck numbers and the 96-, 48-, 19.2- and 16-year Fourier constituents. A review of Figures 11, 12, 13, 14

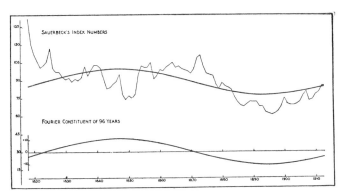

FIGURE 11. Sauerbeck's index numbers of general wholesale prices.
Equation to the upper smooth curve: $y = 88.6 + 11.2 \sin (\frac{360^\circ}{96} t + 342^\circ)$,
origin at 1818.

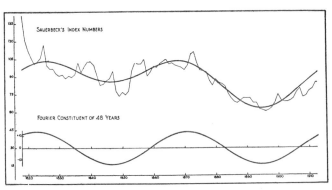

FIGURE 12. Sauerbeck's index numbers of general wholesale prices.
Equation to the upper smooth curve: $y = 88.6 + 11.2 \sin (\frac{360^\circ}{96} t + 342^\circ) +$
$13.8 \sin (\frac{360^\circ}{48} t + 55^\circ)$, origin at 1818.

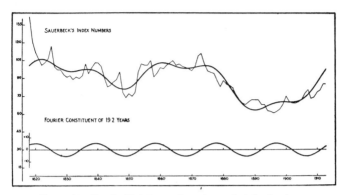

FIGURE 13. Sauerbeck's index numbers of general wholesale prices.
Equation to the upper smooth curve: $y = 88.6 + 11.2 \sin(\frac{360°}{96}t + 342°) + 13.8 \sin(\frac{360°}{48}t + 55°) + 5.3 \sin(\frac{360°}{19.2}t + 52°)$, origin at 1818.

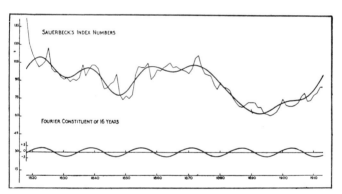

FIGURE 14. Sauerbeck's index numbers of general wholesale prices.
Equation to the upper smooth curve: $y = 88.6 + 11.2 \sin(\frac{360°}{96}t + 342°) + 13.8 \sin(\frac{360°}{48}t + 55°) + 5.3 \sin(\frac{360°}{19.2}t + 52°) + 3.6 \sin(\frac{360°}{16}t + 343°)$, origin at 1818.

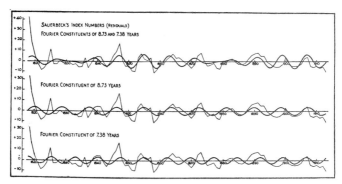

FIGURE 15.   Residuals of Sauerbeck's index numbers of general wholesale prices.
Equation to the upper smooth curve: $y = 3.8 \sin \left(\frac{360^\circ}{8.73}t + 9^\circ\right) +$
$3.1 \sin \left(\frac{360^\circ}{7.38}t + 92^\circ\right)$, origin at 1818.
Middle smooth curve: $y = 3.8 \sin \left(\frac{360^\circ}{8.73}t + 9^\circ\right)$.
Bottom smooth curve: $y = 3.1 \sin \left(\frac{360^\circ}{7.38}t + 92^\circ\right)$.

exemplifies how the addition of Fourier terms gives an increasingly accurate description of the general trend of the Sauerbeck numbers. The compound curve in Figure 14, I have regarded as the general trend of the Sauerbeck numbers. If the ordinates of this compound curve corresponding to the years between 1818 and 1913 are subtracted from the Sauerbeck index numbers for those years, we obtain what I have called the Sauerbeck residuals, which are listed in Table III and are graphed in Figure 15.

Table II, as we have seen, indicates that there is a real cycle between 8.73 and 7.38 years in the Sauerbeck index numbers. In Figure 15, three smooth curves have been fitted to the Sauerbeck residuals, one of which is made up of the two cycles of 8.73 and 7.38 years respectively. This curve gives an excellent description of the residuals. In the remaining curves the cycles of 8.73

and 7.38 years have been fitted to the data separately. The curve of 8.73 years, as we should expect from the greater value of A^2 in Table II, gives a better description of the residuals than the curve of 7.38 years.

Crop Cycles as Generating Cycles

No one familiar with the theory of prices and with the multitudinous causes of change would expect the record of general wholesale prices to show an exact mathematical precision in the working out of any one cause. If there were a predominant cause one would feel that, at best, the nature of its effect would be revealed only in the average of a fairly long record. One would be prepared for a marked deviation from the average in any particular instance. On the other hand, if in the average of a fairly long record there should be evidence of a persistent cycle, no one acquainted with the statistical theory of cycles would fail to suspect the presence of a predominant periodic cause.

The analysis of a century of wholesale prices has revealed the existence of a cycle of about eight years in length. What is its cause?

I have shown that in the United States the yield per acre of the leading crops between 1882 and 1918 passed through cycles of about eight years with maxima at about 1882, 1890, 1898, 1906, and 1914. These eight-year cycles in the yield of the crops generated eight-year cycles in the prices of organic raw materials of manufactures which, according to the law of competitive price, were followed by corresponding cycles in the prices of manufactured commodities. In two earlier articles published in the *Journal of the Royal Statistical Society* the following were among the conclusions that were reached:[1]

(1) The yield per acre of representative crops in the United Kingdom since 1884—when the figures for the yield per acre of the crops began to be collected officially—passed through eight-year cycles which were synchronous with the cycles of eight years in the yield of the American crops;

(2) The yield per acre of representative crops in France was closely correlated with the yield in the United Kingdom and passed through eight-year cycles which were synchronous with the crop cycles in the United Kingdom and in the United States.

The synchronism of the crop cycles in these three countries and the demonstrated existence of derived eight-year cycles of agricultural prices in the United States, which, according to the law of competitive price, induced corresponding cycles in the prices of manufactured commodities, would seem to indicate that the clue to the observed eight-year cycle in Sauerbeck's index numbers of general prices might be found in the eight-year cycles of the crops.

Holding fast to this clue we shall present evidence to show that throughout the interval under investigation, 1818 to 1913, and for a still longer period, the British

[1] "Crop Cycles in the United Kingdom and in the United States," May, 1919; "Crop Cycles in the United Kingdom and in France," May, 1920.

crops passed through cycles of approximately eight years in length.

The first relevant facts have already been adduced. The yield per acre of representative crops in the United Kingdom—wheat, oats, and barley—passed through cycles of eight years with maxima at about 1882, 1890, 1898, 1906, 1914, and these cycles were synchronous with those of France and the United States. (The graph is given in Figure 16.)

In presenting the next remarkable piece of evidence I make use of a thoughtful, long neglected paper [1] on "A Comparison of the Fluctuations in the Price of Wheat and in the Cotton and Silk Imports into Great Britain," by the late J. H. Poynting, at one time Professor of Physics in Birmingham.[2] Having in mind, doubtless, the essays of Stanley Jevons, the author expressed cautiously the opinion that "the attempt to prove the sunspot origin of variations of the harvests and crops has probably led us somewhat away from the proper line of inquiry. This, it seems to me, should begin with such a manipulation of the statistics as to show the true fluctuations whatever they may be, with the effects of wars, increase of commerce, etc., as far as possible eliminated." [3] Accordingly Professor Poynting set about devising a method to reveal the essential fluctuations in the price of wheat in England from 1760 to 1875. Here is his description of the method:

[1] *Journal of the Royal Statistical Society*, March, 1884.

[2] "Poynting belonged to the rare type of men who are more critical of their own work than of that produced by others. The number of his papers is therefore comparatively small, but each of them marks some definite and generally important step." Schuster and Shipley, *Britain's Heritage of Science*, p. 161.

[3] *Journal of the Royal Statistical Society*, March, 1884, p. 35.

" In order to determine the fluctuations we require
to know not only the actual price, but whether that
price is above or below the average *for that time.*
It becomes necessary then to average the prices in
some way so as to obtain a standard for each year, and
we can then determine whether the price for any
particular year is high or low according as it is above
or below that standard. I have found it sufficient
to average for ten years at a time, that is, I have taken
as the standard for each year the average of the
ten years of which that year is the fifth. If a curve
be drawn whose ordinates represent these standard
prices, it will be seen at once that all the larger
irregularities are nearly smoothed down. . . .

" It would now be possible to represent the rises and
falls in price by comparing the price for each year
with the standard for that year. But there are so
many irregularities of short duration, say two or
three years, that it is more convenient to take, instead of the price for each year, the average for a
short period, and for this purpose I adopt four
years. The price for any one year then to be compared with the standard, is the average for the four
years of which that year is the second.

" Were there only very small variations in the
standard, it would be sufficient to take the difference between the ten-yearly and the four-yearly
averages. But the standard varies very considerably
. . . The higher the standard, the greater are the
differences between it and the four-yearly average.
To obtain results which may be compared with each
other at different times, this effect of change of

standard must be eliminated. This may be done by finding what percentage the four-yearly is of the ten-yearly average." [1]

The numerical results of the application of this method to the prices of wheat in England from 1760 to 1875 are given in Table IV and are graphed in Figure 16. After Professor Poynting had made his computations following the method which has just been described and had written his paper, he had the good fortune to have it read, before its publication, by Professor George Gabriel Stokes [2] than whom there was probably no one better equipped to pass judgment upon the mathematical implications of the Poynting method of curve smoothing. Professor Poynting's conclusions from the observations of his eminent critic are given in these summary sentences:

" Thus the effect of the averaging process is practically to destroy all harmonics below five years, to save over half the amplitude at six years, a greater amount up to eight years, when about five-sixths is

[1] *Journal of the Royal Statistical Society,* March, 1884, pp. 36, 37.

[2] "The golden age of mathematics and physics at Cambridge was coincident with the scientific activity of George Gabriel Stokes (1819–1903) which began in 1842, and extended, with but slightly diminished vigor, to the end of the last century. Stokes' position as an investigator is among the greatest, but his influence cannot be measured merely by the record of his published work. He united two generations of scientific workers by the love and veneration centered in their gratitude for the assistance and encouragement which, with kindly and genuine interest, he showered upon them out of the wealth of his knowledge and experience. Even those who intellectually were his equals owed much to his sound and impartial judgment. Turning away from the grave which was closed over his life-long friend, Kelvin was heard to say: 'Stokes is gone, and I shall never return to Cambridge.'" Schuster and Shipley, *Britain's Heritage of Science,* p. 123.

saved, and beyond that a continually decreasing amount, though at fifteen years still nearly one-half is saved. . . . Thus while for eight, nine, and ten-year periods the process saves about 80 per cent of the coefficient, it falls to 60 per cent on the one side for six years, and to 45 per cent on the other for sixteen years." [1]

With this large proportion of the amplitudes of possible cycles between six and sixteen years in length preserved by the process of curve smoothing, one would suppose that the author would have been eager to know whether there was any regularity in his data. But Professor Poynting's caution led him to stop at the most interesting phase of his investigation. The Chairman of the meeting of the Statistical Society at which the paper was read, Sir Rawson W. Rawson, was at pains specifically to point out that "Professor Poynting did not suggest that there were periods, or cycles of prices or of anything similar. He had merely adopted a ten year's period for forming an average, in order to establish a curve for the examination and comparison of periodicities of every kind, and did not suggest that there were periods, or cycles of prices, or anything else." [2]

We now ask the definite question: Is there evidence that cycles in the yield of wheat recurred during the interval from 1760 to 1875?

By the application of the method of the periodogram

[1] *Journal of the Royal Statistical Society*, March, 1884, pp. 46, 47.
[2] *Ibid.*, p. 68.

we have found that in the yield per acre of the leading crops in the United States, in the United Kingdom, and in France, there are cycles of approximately eight years, and these eight-year cycles in the three countries are synchronous. We have also found that the prices of the crops in the United States are closely correlated with the yield per acre, the coefficients of correlation ranging from $r = -.2$ *to* $r = -.9$ and averaging $r = -.7$.

It would, therefore, seem legitimate to assume that if there were cycles in the price of wheat in England from 1760 to 1875, during a large part of which time the importation of grain was restricted in consequence either of wars or of corn laws, then there were cycles of like period and opposite phase in the yield per acre of the crops.

If we compute a sine curve with a period of eight years for the Poynting smoothed index numbers of the price of wheat, which are given in Table IV, we find (Figure 16) that

(1) The curve fits the observations surprisingly well throughout the 116 years of the record except for the interval of the wars of the French Revolution and the Napoleonic wars;

(2) The eight-year cycle in the price of wheat, in consequence of the law of demand, reveals an eight-year cycle in the yield per acre of wheat continuous with the eight-year cycle already established for the crops of the United Kingdom [1]

[1] The data and original graph for the period 1884 to 1914 may be found in the *Journal of the Royal Statistical Society,* May, 1919, pp. 384, 387.

from 1884 to 1914. The continuity of the cycles is shown in Figure 16.

(3) The cycles in the yield per acre of the crops from 1760 to 1913 generated derived cycles in the prices of organic raw materials of production which, in consequence of the law of competitive price, must have tended to induce eight-year cycles in the general prices of commodities;

(4) The analysis of the Sauerbeck index numbers shows that, as a matter of fact, during the century for which the Sauerbeck numbers are given, 1818–1913, general prices did pass through cycles of approximately eight years.

In Figure 16 an eight-year cycle is fitted to the residuals of the Sauerbeck index numbers. We found in our analysis of the Sauerbeck residuals that the equation to the indicated cycle of 8.73 years was

$$y = 3.8 \sin\left(\frac{360°}{8.73}t + 9°\right),$$

and that the equation to the indicated cycle of 7.38 years was $y = 3.1 \sin\left(\frac{360°}{7.38}t + 92°\right)$. The eight-year cycle which is representative of the Sauerbeck residuals in Figure 16 was constructed from these two equations in the following way: Its period of eight years is the mean of the periods of these two cycles $\frac{8.73 + 7.38}{2} = 8.05$; the amplitude of the eight-year cycle is the mean of the amplitudes of these two cycles, $\frac{3.8 + 3.1}{2} = 3.45$;

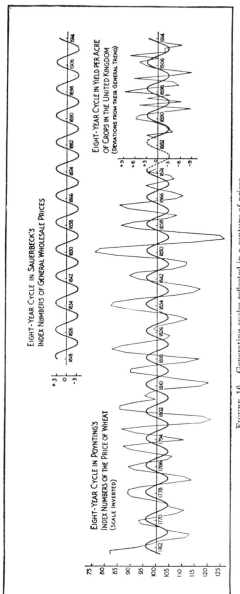

FIGURE 16.   Generating cycles reflected in a century of prices.

Upper curve: $y = 3.5 \sin (\frac{360°}{8} t + 51°)$, origin at 1818.   Derived from the 8.73 and 7.38 years Fourier constituents of Sauerbeck's index numbers.

Lower curves: Poynting's index numbers, $y = 100.2 + 4.4 \sin (\frac{360°}{8} t + 248°)$, origin at 1762;

Yield per acre of the crops, $y = 3.0 \sin (\frac{360°}{8} t + 142°)$, origin at 1884.

and the phase of the eight-year cycle is the mean of the phases of the two cycles $\frac{9° + 92°}{2} = 50° 30'$. It will be seen from Figure 16 that the eight-year cycles in the century of Sauerbeck's index numbers were approximately synchronous with the corresponding cycles in the indicated yield per acre of the British crops. The eight-year cycle in the crops is proved to have persisted throughout nearly the whole period of 159 years from 1760 to 1918 (the investigation of the American crops was carried through 1918) or for an interval of twenty cycles of eight years in length. This generating eight-year cycle in the crops induced derived cycles of prices which are reflected and verified in the century of Sauerbeck index numbers of general wholesale prices.

APPENDIX

TABLE I.—Sauerbeck's Index Numbers of General Wholesale Prices

Year	Index Number	Year	Index Number	Year	Index Number	Year	Index Number
1818	142	1842	91	1866	102	1890	72
1819	121	1843	83	1867	100	1891	72
1820	112	1844	84	1868	99	1892	68
1821	106	1845	87	1869	98	1893	68
1822	101	1846	89	1870	96	1894	63
1823	103	1847	95	1871	100	1895	62
1824	106	1848	78	1872	109	1896	61
1825	117	1849	74	1873	111	1897	62
1826	100	1850	77	1874	102	1898	64
1827	97	1851	75	1875	96	1899	68
1828	97	1852	78	1876	95	1900	75
1829	93	1853	95	1877	94	1901	70
1830	91	1854	102	1878	87	1902	69
1831	92	1855	101	1879	83	1903	69
1832	89	1856	101	1880	88	1904	70
1833	91	1857	105	1881	85	1905	72
1834	90	1858	91	1882	84	1906	77
1835	92	1859	94	1883	82	1907	80
1836	102	1860	99	1884	76	1908	73
1837	94	1861	98	1885	72	1909	74
1838	99	1862	101	1886	69	1910	78
1839	103	1863	103	1887	68	1911	80
1840	103	1864	105	1888	70	1912	85
1841	100	1865	101	1889	72	1913	85

TABLE II.—Results of Fourier Analysis of Sauerbeck's Index
Numbers of General Wholesale Prices. 1818–1913

Di-visor	Period in Years	a	b	A²	Di-visor	Period in Years	a	b	A²
1	96.0	− 3.46	+10.60	124.42	13	7.4	+3.12	− .11	9.74
2	48.0	+11.27	+ 7.96	190.40	14	6.9	+2.12	+1.77	7.62
3	32.0	+ 1.08	+ .76	1.73	15	6.4	+ .61	+ .17	.41
4	24.0	+ 2.95	+ .70	9.17	16	6.0	+1.67	+ .29	2.86
5	19.2	+ 4.18	+ 3.28	28.23	17	5.6	+ .88	+ .72	1.30
6	16.0	− 1.08	+ 3.46	13.13	18	5.3	+ .59	+2.03	4.48
7	13.7	+ .78	+ .76	1.19	19	5.0	+ .04	+ .66	.44
8	12.0	+ 1.85	+ .73	3.95	20	4.8	+ .29	+ .75	.65
9	10.7	+ 1.18	− .02	1.40	21	4.6	+1.38	+ .48	2.14
10	9.6	+ 2.00	− .92	4.86	22	4.4	+ .03	+1.64	2.68
11	8.7	+ .61	+ 3.76	14.52	23	4.2	+ .80	+ .63	1.03
12	8.0	+ 1.36	− .51	2.12	24	4.0	+ .30	− .10	.10

TABLE III.—Residuals of Sauerbeck's Index Numbers
of General Wholesale Prices

Year	Residual	Year	Residual	Year	Residual	Year	Residual
1818	+42.4	1842	— 1.2	1866	+ 3.9	1890	+ 7.7
1819	+17.7	1843	— 5.7	1867	+ 1.2	1891	+ 8.5
1820	+ 5.5	1844	— 0.9	1868	— 1.0	1892	+ 5.2
1821	— 2.6	1845	+ 5.3	1869	— 3.2	1893	+ 5.2
1822	— 8.4	1846	+ 9.7	1870	— 6.6	1894	— 0.5
1823	— 6.3	1847	+17.0	1871	— 2.8	1895	— 2.4
1824	— 1.7	1848	+ 0.2	1872	+ 5.9	1896	— 4.7
1825	+11.6	1849	— 4.8	1873	+ 8.2	1897	— 5.3
1826	— 2.4	1850	— 4.1	1874	+ 0.3	1898	— 5.0
1827	— 2.4	1851	— 9.0	1875	— 4.3	1899	— 2.5
1828	+ 0.4	1852	— 9.5	1876	— 3.3	1900	+ 3.2
1829	— 1.3	1853	+ 3.7	1877	— 1.9	1901	— 2.9
1830	— 1.8	1854	+ 7.3	1878	— 6.3	1902	— 4.5
1831	— 0.4	1855	+ 2.5	1879	— 7.5	1903	— 4.7
1832	— 3.6	1856	+ 1.0	1880	+ 0.5	1904	— 4.1
1833	— 2.8	1857	+ 3.6	1881	+ 0.3	1905	— 2.4
1834	— 5.6	1858	—10.9	1882	+ 2.0	1906	+ 2.1
1835	— 5.3	1859	— 7.9	1883	+ 2.7	1907	+ 4.1
1836	+ 3.0	1860	— 2.1	1884	— 0.7	1908	— 4.4
1837	— 6.2	1861	— 2.2	1885	— 2.4	1909	— 5.8
1838	— 1.5	1862	+ 1.8	1886	— 2.9	1910	— 4.8
1839	+ 3.2	1863	+ 4.8	1887	— 1.7	1911	— 6.5
1840	+ 4.9	1864	+ 7.2	1888	+ 2.3	1912	— 5.7
1841	+ 4.5	1865	+ 3.3	1889	+ 6.1	1913	—10.2

TABLE IV.—POYNTING INDEX NUMBERS OF THE PRICE OF WHEAT
PER QUARTER IN ENGLAND FROM 1760 TO 1875.

M_{10} = TEN-YEAR AVERAGE OF THE ABSOLUTE PRICES OF WHEAT

M_4 = FOUR-YEAR AVERAGE OF THE ABSOLUTE PRICES OF WHEAT

Year	Poynting Index M_4/M_{10}	Year	Poynting Index M_4/M_{10}	Year	Poynting Index M_4/M_{10}	Year	Poynting Index M_4/M_{10}
1760	82.3	1789	106.0	1818	116.6	1847	111.6
1761	82.2	1790	98.5	1819	103.5	1848	103.6
1762	92.1	1791	90.0	1820	87.9	1849	84.2
1763	98.1	1792	87.1	1821	82.6	1850	75.9
1764	101.8	1793	98.1	1822	86.2	1851	78.0
1765	111.6	1794	110.7	1823	95.0	1852	94.8
1766	112.9	1795	102.3	1824	103.3	1853	112.9
1767	104.8	1796	91.9	1825	105.0	1854	126.4
1768	101.4	1797	86.4	1826	101.7	1855	124.6
1769	94.3	1798	97.0	1827	98.6	1856	108.5
1770	93.3	1799	117.4	1828	100.9	1857	92.2
1771	100.2	1800	121.1	1829	107.0	1858	86.8
1772	107.7	1801	117.8	1830	111.7	1859	91.4
1773	110.7	1802	98.4	1831	107.8	1860	103.0
1774	105.3	1803	85.7	1832	100.2	1861	107.7
1775	103.8	1804	85.7	1833	87.6	1862	99.2
1776	98.3	1805	91.3	1834	82.3	1863	88.8
1777	90.5	1806	99.7	1835	83.3	1864	85.3
1778	88.9	1807	95.4	1836	91.9	1865	96.2
1779	89.2	1808	97.6	1837	105.8	1866	107.2
1780	93.9	1809	101.7	1838	114.2	1867	110.0
1781	104.8	1810	116.8	1839	117.0	1868	105.8
1782	113.6	1811	120.3	1840	111.4	1869	99.3
1783	111.0	1812	108.8	1841	101.5	1870	95.5
1784	101.7	1813	100.3	1842	92.9	1871	101.0
1785	91.6	1814	89.8	1843	89.4	1872	106.5
1786	89.1	1815	90.0	1844	92.4	1873	104.7
1787	95.3	1816	97.8	1845	106.1	1874	96.4
1788	104.2	1817	111.3	1846	111.1	1875	99.8

CHAPTER IV

THE ORIGIN OF THE EIGHT-YEAR GENERATING CYCLE [1]

Summary

The persistence of the eight-year generating cycle in England for one hundred and sixty years; the congruence of the eight-year crop cycles in England, France, and the United States; the persistence of the eight-year meteorological cycles, and their congruence in Europe and America; the congruence of the economic and meteorological cycles—these uniformities and agreements suggest that their cause must be sought in a cosmical cycle. The probable cause is the planet Venus in its eight-yearly periodic motion with respect to the Earth and the Sun.

GENERATING economic cycles are to be described as economic cycles that have their origin in non-economic causes and become the originating source of derived economic cycles. The theory of generating cycles embraces three fundamental inquiries: first, as to the existence of generating cycles, their length, amplitudes and phases; second, as to the ways in which the generating cycles work out their rhythmic effects in remote parts of economic life; and third, as to the cause of generating cycles. In previous chapters I have dealt with the first and second of these divisions. We must now attempt to place the cause of the eight-year generating cycle.

[1] This chapter was first published, substantially in its present form, in the *Quarterly Journal of Economics*, November, 1921.

Economic Cycles

If index numbers of the annual yield per acre of American crops are plotted for a considerable period, from 1882 to the present time, for example, the graph will be a composite of three types of changes—secular, cyclical, and random—which were long ago classified and described by Cournot. In Chapter II, I eliminated the secular changes in the yield per acre of the six

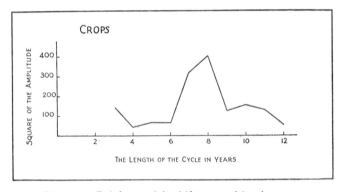

FIGURE 17.　Periodogram of the yield per acre of American crops.

leading crops in American agriculture, and then formed index numbers of their percentage deviations from the respective secular trends. The series of index numbers was then scrutinized with a view to finding evidence of a real, recurring cycle, and Figure 17 shows that of all possible cycles between three and twelve years in the index numbers of the yield per acre of the crops, the most probable length is in the neighborhood of eight years. If an eight-year cycle is fitted, by the method of least squares, to the index numbers of yield, the maxima of the repeated cycle fall, approximately,

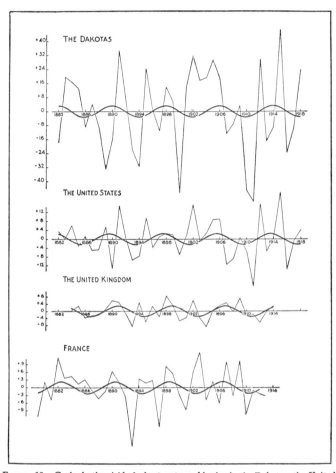

FIGURE 18.   Cycles in the yield of wheat, oats, and barley in the Dakotas, the United
States, the United Kingdom, and France.

The Dakotas: $y = 3.20 \sin (\frac{360^\circ}{8}t + 93^\circ\,59')$, origin at 1882;

The United States: $y = 2.49 \sin (\frac{360^\circ}{8}t + 111^\circ\,27')$, origin at 1882;

The United Kingdom: $y = 3.02 \sin (\frac{360^\circ}{8}t + 142^\circ\,0')$, origin at 1884;

France: $y = 2.17 \sin (\frac{360^\circ}{8}t + 292^\circ\,56')$, origin at 1879.

at 1882, 1890, 1898, 1906, 1914. In other studies [1] referring to the Dakotas, the United States, the United Kingdom, and France, the eight-year cycles were isolated and were found to be practically synchronous in these countries. Figure 18 shows the graph descriptive of the eight-year cycles in the yield of wheat, oats, and barley.

With the existence of an international cycle in the yield of the crops firmly established, an obvious corollary suggested that according to the law of demand— in consequence of which the price tends to fall with an increase in the supply of the commodity—there should be a derived eight-year cycle in the prices of farm products. Accordingly, the law of demand for the six representative American crops was ascertained, and the derived cycle of prices of farm products was computed from the established eight-year cycles in the yield of the crops. The results are presented in Figure 19, together with a comparison between the actual index numbers of prices and the forecast indices of prices.

After ascertaining that the prices of agricultural products do actually vary inversely with the yield in a definite, predictable way, it became possible to subject the theory of the existence of generating cycles of crops to a severe critical test. If the prices of agricultural commodities do vary inversely with the yield, and if there is a real cycle of eight years in the yield of the crops, then the record of prices throughout a long inter-

[1] "Crop-Cycles in the United Kingdom and in the United States," *Journal of the Royal Statistical Society*, May, 1919; "Crop-Cycles in the United Kingdom and in France," *ibid.*, May, 1920; "Forecasting the Crops of the Dakotas," *Political Science Quarterly*, June, 1920, particularly pp. 228, 229.

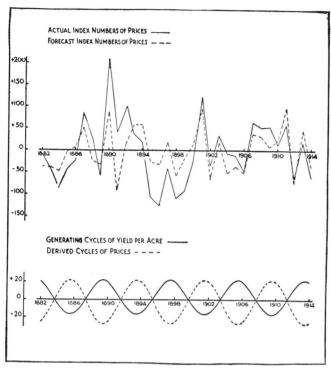

FIGURE 19

Upper part: Actual index numbers of prices of the six representative crops and the
index numbers of prices forecast from the index numbers of the yield
per acre by means of the formula

$$y = -1.295x - .02.$$

Lower part: Generating cycles of the yield per acre of the crops,

$$y = 1.6 + 20.0 \sin (45°t + 109°), \text{ origin at } 1882;$$

Derived cycles of prices of the crops computed from the generating cycles
of yield by means of the formula,

$$y = -1.295x - .02.$$

val should reveal the existence of the eight-year generating cycle of crops. Moreover, if the generating cycle is
a persistent, real cycle, then the cycle of yield per acre
that is revealed indirectly by the record of prices
throughout a long interval should be the same as the
cycle that is obtained directly from the more recent

official estimates of the actual yield per acre. Figure 20 shows not only that the record of prices in England from 1760 to 1875 exhibits a clear-cut cycle of eight years in the yield per acre, but also that the cycle is continuous with the eight-year cycle which is established directly from the official estimates of the crop yields since 1884.

The theory of the generating cycle also requires that the movement of general prices should follow the rhythmic changes in the yield of agricultural products. As nearly all foods are derived either directly or indirectly from the farms, and as eighty per cent of the raw materials of manufactures—according to the United States census of 1900—are organic raw materials produced on the farms, the movement of general prices should reflect the rhythm in the yield of the crops. The theory of the relation between the generating cycles of crops and the movement of general prices was subjected to a searching empirical test. Sauerbeck's index numbers of general prices, covering the interval of nearly a century between the Napoleonic wars and the Great War, were examined by means of Fourier analysis with a view to discovering real periodicities. The analysis showed that if there were a sequence of real cycles in the century of prices in England, the most probable length of the constituent cycle was approximately eight years. When this cycle of general prices was computed and plotted, its graph was found to be practically congruent with the graph of the yield of wheat determined indirectly from the record of wheat prices from 1760 to 1875, and practically congruent with the graph of the cycles in the

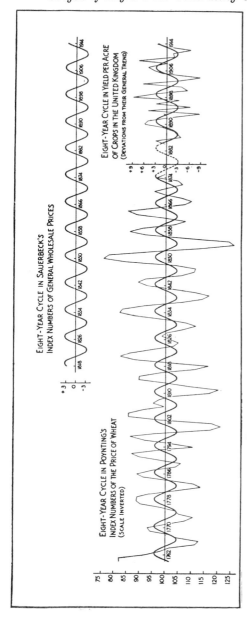

FIGURE 20. Generating cycles reflected in a century of prices.

Upper curve: $y = 3.5 \sin \left(\frac{360°}{8} t + 51°\right)$, origin at 1818. Derived from the 8.73 and 7.38 years Fourier constituents of Sauerbeck's index numbers.

Lower curves: Poynting's index numbers, $y = 100\,2 + 4.4 \sin \left(\frac{360°}{8} t + 248°\right)$, origin at 1762;

Yield per acre of the crops, $y = 3.0 \sin \left(\frac{360°}{8} t + 142°\right)$, origin at 1884.

yield of the crops determined directly from the official estimates of the annual yield of the crops since 1884. The graphs are given in Figure 20.

Meteorological Cycles

In 1919 the Carnegie Institution published *Climatic Cycles and Tree-Growth*, by A. E. Douglass. With the hope of throwing some light on the periodic activity of the sun, Professor Douglass, by training and profession an astronomer, undertook this laborious and valuable investigation of the variation in the size of the rings of trees, which, he assumed, was a consequence of meteorological changes having their origin in solar activity. He selected for his first studies yellow pines taken from the forests of northern Arizona. As there is, for the most part, a scant and variable rainfall throughout the state, Professor Douglass assumed as a working theory (1) that the growth of pines in that region depends largely upon the available water; (2) that the rings of the pines measure the growth of the trees; (3) that the rings form a measure of annual precipitation.

The rainfall of Arizona is extremely variable from station to station. "Storms come from the Pacific coast and rain occurs a day or so later than in southern California. Spring and autumn are the dry seasons, and the warmest time of the year is usually in June, just before the summer rains begin. The summer rains occur in July and August and often come in 'spells' that last a week or two, with thunderstorms in the afternoons or at night, followed by clear mornings. Unlike the winter storms, the summer rains are local and apt to be torrential in character, with heavy run-off." The San Francisco Peaks, about ten miles north of Flagstaff, "illustrate how meteorological data may vary in rugged localities. The west slopes of these mountains are exposed to the westerly storms and have an immense snowfall. Springs abound, and all favorable localities are taken up as ranches. East of the mountain, however, the land is dry and barren, and long distances intervene between watering places. . . . In a very rugged country like that about Prescott similar differences between east and west mountain slopes must constantly occur."

The longest meteorological record in the Arizona pine forest was begun at Whipple Barracks, near Prescott, in 1867, and then continued at Prescott, which has an elevation of about 5200 feet. With the variability of rainfall from station to station which we have just noted, and with the change of the meteorological observation from Whipple Barracks to Prescott, one would scarcely expect any normality to be revealed in this particular rainfall record. An examination of Figure 21 is, nevertheless, surprisingly suggestive. The top graph[1] shows the relation between the annual rainfall and the growth of pines near Prescott. The growth seems to show a secular trend downwards and for that reason, in seeking the degree of relation between the annual rainfall and the annual growth, I have computed the correlation between their first differences. The measure of this relation is $r = .56$, which shows that there is an unmistakable relation between the rainfall and the growth of pines in this region.

[1] The top graph is taken from Professor Douglass' work, p. 29.

Is the rainfall itself subject to law? In the lower part of Figure 21 an eight-year cycle is fitted to the annual rainfall data, and we find that the maxima occur at 1866, 1874, 1882, 1890, 1898, 1906—which makes the Prescott rainfall, during this interval, synchronous

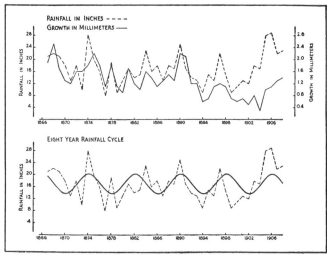

FIGURE 21.   Cycles in the rainfall and in the growth of pines near Prescott, Arizona. Equation to the rainfall cycle, $y = 16.9 + 3.2 \sin (\frac{360°}{8} t + 127° \, 12')$, origin at 1867.

with the crop cycles in the United States, in the United Kingdom, and in France. Gratifying as this result is, I should not attach importance to it—because of the meteorological record being made up of observations at two different stations in a country in which the rainfall is notoriously variable from station to station—but for its relation to what is about to be described.

Flagstaff, in Arizona, is about 67 miles north of Prescott. From the magnificent pine forests about Flagstaff Professor Douglass was able to obtain cuttings from trees which supplied him with a continuous history of rings for 500 years. Referring to these Flagstaff pines, Professor Douglass makes these statements as to the cyclical variations in their growth: "The interval from 1830 to the present time divides . . . fairly well in (a period) of 7.3 years" (p. 108). As to the whole record of 500 years, he says, "a 7-year period is also frequently observed" (p. 101). In Table 8 (p. 108) Professor Douglass indicates that this cycle of approxi-

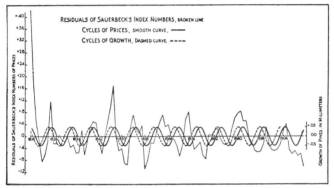

FIGURE 22. Cycles in the residuals of Sauerbeck's index numbers of general wholesale prices in England and in the growth of pines near Flagstaff, Arizona.

Equation to the cycle of prices, —— : $y = 3.1 \sin (\frac{360^\circ}{7.38} t + 92^\circ)$, origin at 1818;

Equation to the cycle of growth, - - - - : $y = .05 \sin (\frac{360^\circ}{7.33} t + 137^\circ 57')$, origin at 1818.

mately 7.3 years has been continuous since 1817. By an odd coincidence Sauerbeck's index numbers of general prices in England begin just one year later, in 1818. In the analysis of the Sauerbeck numbers we found that the eight-year cycle was the mean of two cycles, one of about 8.7 and the other of about 7.38 years. In Figure 22 the smooth graph records the 7.38-year cycle in Sauerbeck's index numbers, and the dashed graph,[1]

[1] The data to which the cycle was fitted covered the 88 years from 1818 to 1905 and were taken from Professor Douglass' work, p 113.

the Douglass 7.3-year cycle in the Arizona pines. The two graphs, considering the errors in the estimated lengths of the cycles, are practically congruent, and from 1867 to 1910 the Douglass 7.3-year cycles in tree growth at Flagstaff run well with the eight-year cycles in the rainfall at Prescott.

The close relation between meteorological cycles and crop cycles is informingly illustrated in the crops of the spring-wheat area in the United States. In 1916, among the states of the United States, North Dakota ranked first in the production of spring wheat, second in the production of barley, and seventh in the production of oats; and to these three crops, in 1918, seventy per cent of its crop area was devoted. The semi-arid region of the United States begins to the west of the one-hundredth meridian, and this meridian divides nearly in two the state of North Dakota. The average precipitation does not greatly exceed the minimum essential for vegetation, and, consequently, we find a close correlation between the crop yield and the rainfall of the critical months, which are May and June. The correlation coefficients [1] between the rainfall of May and June and the yield of the crops are, for wheat, $r = .66$; for oats, $r = .79$; and for barley, $r = .73$.

With this close relation between rainfall and crop yields established for this very important, semi-arid agricultural region, one is again led to inquire whether the rainfall itself is not subject to law.[2] The rainfall

[1] "Forecasting the Crops of the Dakotas," *Political Science Quarterly*, June, 1920, p. 219.

[2] This question I have treated in a paper on "Forecasting the Crops of the Dakotas," *Political Science Quarterly*, June, 1920.

records of North Dakota and South Dakota, for May
and June, from 1882 to 1918 were searched for evidence
of periodicity between the limits of three and twelve
years, and the result indicated that, if there is a real
cycle of rainfall for May and June in these two representative states its most probable value is in the neighborhood of eight years. When an eight-year cycle is
fitted to the rainfall data, the maxima occur, approximately, at 1882, 1890, 1898, 1906, 1914, and are practically synchronous with the dates of the maxima of
rainfall of Prescott, Arizona, the growth of pines in
Arizona, and the maxima of the international crop
cycles in the United States, in the United Kingdom,
and in France. The graph of the Dakota rainfall is
given in Figure 23.

Starting from the hypothesis that American economic
activity is largely dependent in its ebb and flow upon
the prosperity of the agricultural Middle West, I sought,
in an early study [1] of meteorological cycles, to discover
a periodicity in the rainfall of the Mississippi Valley.
As the meteorological records were much longer for the
Ohio Valley than for the states further west, the rainfall
of the Ohio Valley was made the basis of the first examination. The method employed was a test of the
possible presence of cycles between the limits of three
and thirty-three years, and the evidence was unmistakable. If there is a real cycle of rainfall in the Ohio
Valley its most probable length is about eight years
and its maxima are approximately synchronous with
the maxima of the May and June rainfall of the Dakotas,
the annual rainfall of Prescott, Arizona, the growth

[1] *Economic Cycles: Their Law and Cause,* 1914.

of pines in Arizona, and the international crop cycles
to which we have so frequently referred. The graph
is given in Figure 23.

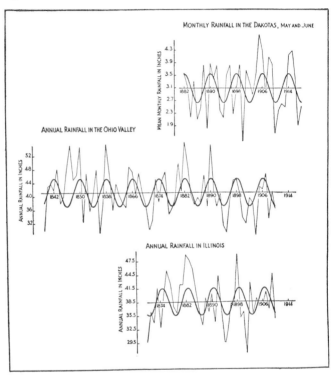

FIGURE 23.   Cycles in the rainfall of the Dakotas, of the Ohio Valley, and of Illinois.
Dakota cycle: $y = 3.09 + 0.45 \sin (\frac{360°}{8}t + 84° \, 39')$, origin at 1882;
Ohio cycle: $y = 41.2 + 4.13 \sin (\frac{360°}{8}t + 310° \, 41')$, origin at 1839;
Illinois cycle: $y = 38.5 + 3.05 \sin (\frac{360°}{8}t + 241° \, 52')$, origin at 1870.

At the time of the publication of the essay *Economic
Cycles*, 1914, Illinois was regarded as our leading
cereal-producing state, ranking first in the production
of corn and second in the production of oats. Rainfall
records for many stations in that state were available

for a period of 41 years, from 1870 to 1910. The correlation between the rainfall in the Ohio Valley and the rainfall of Illinois was $r = .60$, and the eight-year cycle in the Ohio Valley rainfall was repeated in an eight-year cycle in the rainfall of Illinois. The graph is likewise given in Figure 23.

In October, 1920, H. W. Clough of the United States Weather Bureau published in the *Monthly Weather Review* an article on "An Approximate Seven-Year Period in Terrestrial Weather, with Solar Correlation." From this paper I make use of two facts: the first refers to atmospheric pressure at Toronto, in Canada, and at St. Louis, in the United States. In Mr. Clough's paper a graph is given of atmospheric pressure at Toronto from about 1843 to 1911, and a similar graph is given for the pressure at St. Louis from about 1874 to about 1917. An inspection of these shows (1) that for the interval covered by the two graphs, they are approximately congruent; (2) that the maxima occur, approximately at 1850, 1858, 1866, 1874, 1882, 1890, 1898, 1914, and are therefore synchronous with the economic and meteorological cycles already examined.

The other fact that I take from Mr. Clough's paper refers to atmospheric pressure in Europe. "Mauer (*Archives des Sci. Phys. Nat.*, Geneva, May, 1918) called attention to a well-marked periodicity of seven to eight years in the winter pressure in Central Europe, with maxima as follows: 1818–19, 1827–28, 1835–36, 1843–44, 1850–51, 1857–58, 1865–66, 1873–74, 1881–82, 1889–90, 1897–98, 1904–05, 1912–13."

If now the dates of the maxima in Mauer's European

pressures are compared with Clough's in America, it will be seen (1) that they are approximately synchronous; (2) that the common interval between the maxima is about eight years; (3) that they are approximately synchronous with the maxima of the crop cycles in the United States, in the United Kingdom, and in France; (4) that they are approximately synchronous with the cycles in Sauerbeck's index numbers from 1818 to 1914.

The next evidence of meteorological cycles is found in an official publication by the United States Weather Bureau. In 1901 the United States took "the lead in reducing its barometric observations to a standard system." [1] The work was conducted by Professor F. H. Bigelow and included "a reëxamination of the various elevations, the local and instrumental errors, the reduction of the station pressures to a homogeneous system, and the preparation of normal tables and charts of pressure, temperature, and vapor pressure at sea level and at the 3,500 foot and 10,000 foot planes." [2] This monumental work bears the title *Report on the Barometry of the United States, Canada, and the West Indies,* and constitutes volume II of the *Report of the Chief of the United States Weather Bureau, 1900, 1901.*

After the completion of this Report with the reduced and standardized material, it became possible for the first time to combine the many thousands of observations that had been made in the United States since the beginning, in about 1870, of the systematic work of official weather observation. The tremendous impor-

[1] Prefatory note in vol. ii of *Report of the Chief of the Weather Bureau,* 1900, 1901.

[2] *Report of the Chief of the Weather Bureau,* 1900–01, vol. i, p. 12.

tance of this great increase in the utilizable meteorological observations is shown in what is, I think, the most pregnant conclusion of Professor Bigelow's Report. I shall quote that conclusion at length and invite particular attention to a few sentences which I have put in italics. The table referred to in the quotation is one in which the final mean pressures for the whole of the United States and for the several constituent large sections are presented. In detail, the barometric pressure series upon which the generalization was based were obtained from the following sections: North Atlantic, South Atlantic, Lake Region, Pacific, West Gulf, North Plateau, South Plateau, and from the records of these regions all combined into a general mean. The pregnant quotation is now given:

" We are at once struck by the remarkable fact, which constitutes an *important discovery in barometric science*, that the secular variations of the barometer from year to year are by no means accidental but a phenomenon of definite proportions. In looking over the tables it is seen that for certain years the barometric reading is persistently lower than the average of the series, and for certain other years it remains higher than the average. This fact is indicated, generally, by each station in the group, most conspicuously for the year 1878. The residuals of that year are persistently minus, about –0.050 inch *for each station in every group for the entire United States;* for the year 1883 they are as persistently plus, about +0.020 inch. This constitutes a range of 0.070 inch, and when we consider that the annual range in the barometer, due to the change of the sun in latitude from $+23°$ to $-23°$, causing the change in the seasons, the difference between winter and summer, is shown by Table 54 to be about 0.100 inch, we conclude that *we are dealing with a phenomenon which at times is seven-tenths of the annual departure in its intensity.* The fact is that the barometric pressure is sometimes maintained higher than the average throughout the entire year over a large continental area in middle latitudes, and that it often equals at least half as much as the influences of the sun's action on the atmosphere by departing 23 degrees in latitude from the equator; in other years the pressure is kept lower than the average by a similar amount. *The years of maximum pressure are 1874–75, 1882–3, 1890, 1896–7, with an interval of about 8 years between them successively; the years of minimum pressure are 1878, 1884–5, 1893, also having an interval of about 8 years. . . ."*

" In seeking for the causes of this phenomenon, I confess that it has been difficult to assign one which is satisfactory. It cannot be a wave motion because the duration of each wave is too long to admit of anything resembling propagation. One suspects that there may be a tilting of the atmosphere from one continent to another, or from one hemisphere to the other, but when we consider the rapid motion of the upper strata of the atmosphere, it does not appear how it can so far deviate from its usual paths as to leave an entire continent lower or higher than the average for so long a time. *One may also suspect purely cosmical causes* due to the variable solar output; indeed, these barometric variations do closely follow the variations in the sunspot frequency and the other products of the sun's variable activity. From 1873 to 1890 there is a remarkable agreement between these two classes of phenomena, *but if the pressure period is 8 years and the sunspot period 11 years that connection cannot be complete in its nature.* It is evident that we shall be obliged to prosecute this study yet further by constructing similar barometric tables for other countries, in each hemisphere, and also that it will be well to include in our research some account of the temperature, the vapor tension, and the magnetic and electric fields of the atmosphere before attempting any further remarks on the subject. . . .

" Finally, it is evident that for the United States we can now correlate the years which have similar secular variations, as 1878, 1885, and 1893, and study them climatologically to see if there are any marked and prevailing features which characterize them. *It is clear that this discussion opens to us for the first time the prospect of a scientific basis for seasonal forecasts,* certainly so if it should prove to be the case that the maximum-pressure years differ distinctly from the minimum-pressure years in their seasonal character, for in the event of our happening on a maximum year we could then predict the feature due to a falling barometer, or, if we are in a minimum year, to a rising barometer, at least for one or two years ahead." [1]

[1] *Report of the Chief of the Weather Bureau*, 1900, 1901, vol. ii, pp. 1004, 1005.

Upon the preceding passages I make these notes:

(1) As far back as 1901 the United States Weather Bureau isolated a cycle in the barometric pressure of the United States;

(2) That cycle was an eight-year cycle which was synchronous with the cycles in economics and meteorology to which constant reference has been made in this essay;

(3) Professor Bigelow regarded the isolation of the cycle as "an important discovery in barometric science," the discussion of which "opens to us for the first time the prospect of a scientific basis for seasonal forecasts";

(4) Professor Bigelow suspected a cosmical cause of the phenomenon, but known solar periodicities failed to satisfy the conditions: "if the pressure period is 8 years and the sun-spot period is 11 years that connection cannot be complete in its nature."

What is the cosmical cause of the eight-year cycle? [1]

The Cause of the Eight-Year Generating Cycle

Is there a cosmical cycle of approximately eight years in length, the effects of which upon the Earth might account for the observed meteorological cycles? Let us divide this question into two and ask (1) is there a cosmical cycle of eight years in length which is synchronous with the observed meteorological cycles? (2) is there reason for believing that the cosmical cycle

[1] This chapter was first printed in 1921. Since then I have shown that the annual rainfall in the United States as a unit, according to the records of about two hundred stations, passes through the same eight-year cycle. See the discussion in Chapter I.

is accompanied with a synchronously varying force that could produce the observed meteorological cycles?

The first question may be answered definitely and positively: there is a cosmical cycle of about eight years that is synchronous with the economic and meteorological cycles the existence of which has already been established.

Perhaps the best way to approach its description is to consider these facts: the maximum visibility of Venus is produced by its greatest phase, its greatest elongation from the sun, and the clearness of our atmosphere, and that maximum tends to recur at intervals of eight years. "Vénus passe tous les huit ans par ses périodes de plus grand éclat (1889–1897–1905–1913). Elle est alors si brillante qu'elle porte ombre comme un petit clair de lune, et il est facile de s'en assurer soit en se plaçant dans une pièce obscure, soit en marchant devant un mur à la campagne. On peut la distinguer en plein jour, à l'œil nu, non seulement avant le coucher du soleil, mais à midi même, lorsque l'on sait où elle est. Aucune étoile ni aucune planète n'atteint un éclat comparable à celui-la." [1] Here is an eight-year cycle in which the dates of maxima are a little in advance of our economic and meteorological cycle. It is not the cycle that we want, but it is closely related to the one for which we are in search.

Before passing to a detailed consideration of the Venus cycle a prejudice must be noted and, if possible, removed. In suggesting that the variability in the brilliance of Venus may have some possible relation to terrestrial affairs one is reminded at once of the

[1] Camille Flammarion, *Rêves étoilés*, pp. 132, 133.

disdainful attitude of Laplace: "Vénus surpasse en clarté les autres planètes et les étoiles; elle est quelque-fois si brillante, qu'on la voit en plein jour, à la vue simple. Ce phénomène, qui revient assez souvent, ne manque jamais d'exciter une vive surprise; et le vulgaire, dans sa crédule ignorance, le suppose toujours lié aux événements contemporains les plus remarquables."[1] Now with regard to this remark, the substance of which is repeated by others in pamphlets and treatises, these comments should be made:

(1) Laplace's scorn was directed towards the prognosticators who encouraged the belief that particular, isolated events were predictable from the aspect of Venus.

(2) Until many years after the death of Laplace, economic and meteorological observations had not been carried sufficiently far to admit of the isolation of long-time cycles showing mean results which could be associated with cosmical variations.

(3) Many physicists and astronomers of unquestioned sanity and proven ability have attempted to discover the effect of Venus upon the position and frequency of sunspots. If that is not a visionary inquiry when Venus is nearly three times further from the Sun than it is from the Earth, the consideration of the possible effects of that planet upon the weather of the Earth should not be regarded as a preposterous undertaking.

Returning now to the question of the periodicity in the motion of Venus with respect to the Earth let us first recall that the relative distances of the Earth and

[1] Laplace, *Exposition du système du monde*, Livre premier, chap. v.

Venus from the Sun are as 1000 to 723; that the orbits of both planets are nearly circular; and that in size, Venus of all the planets most nearly approaches the Earth, its diameter being 7630 miles as compared with the 7918 miles of the Earth.

Let Figure 24 represent the orbits of Venus and the Earth, the orbits being assumed, for the sake of simplicity, to be circles. At this stage no account is taken of the inclination of the plane of the orbit of Venus, which will be considered later on. The following simple description of when and where the two planets are in conjunction is given by R. A. Proctor in his *Transits of Venus:*

" Imagine that a straight pointer from the Sun to Venus, extending to the Earth's orbit, like the line SVE, is carried round S as a central pivot by the motion of the planet Venus. Then whenever this pointer comes up to the Earth, the three bodies— Sun, Earth, and Venus—are in conjunction. Now, Venus travels with a mean motion of 96′ 7″.8 per day around the Sun (completing a revolution in 224.701 days), while the Earth travels with a mean motion of 59′ 8″.3 (completing a revolution in 365.257 days); so that in each mean solar day Venus gains, on the average, 36′ 59″.5 upon the Earth. This is the rate at which our imaginary pointer, starting from a position such as SVE, sweeps onwards from the advancing Earth, so as to again reach the Earth by overtaking it, just as the minute-hand of a clock, after being in conjunction with the hour-hand, passes on towards its next conjunction, with the *excess* of its motion over the hour-hand. We have only, then, to ask how long it will take the pointer, with its mean daily gain of 36′ 59″.5, to gain one complete circuit, to have the interval in time between successive conjunctions of the Earth and Venus—

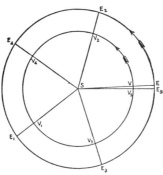

FIGURE 24.   Illustration of the conjunctions of the Earth and Venus.

in other words, there will be just as many days in this interval as the number of times 36′ 59″.5 is contained in 360°, or, reducing both to seconds, as 2219.5 is contained in 1,296,000. The division . . . gives us 583.9 days.

" Our Venus-carried pointer thus takes 583.9 days in overtaking the Earth. This is more than a year by about 218.6 days, in which period, with her mean motion of 59′ 8″.3 per day, the Earth travels round nearly $215\frac{1}{2}$ degrees. Now, 216 degrees would be $\frac{3}{5}$ of a complete circuit. We see, then, that the next conjunction-line must be set almost exactly $\frac{3}{5}$ of the way round from SVE, or in the position SV_1E_1; the next will have the position SV_2E_2; the third will have the position SV_3E_3; the fourth, the position SV_4E_4; and the fifth will be close up to SVE, in the position SV_5E_5, about $2\frac{1}{2}$ degrees behind SVE.

" Since the interval between each conjunction is about a year and three-fifths, the whole time occupied before the position SV_5E_5 is reached by the conjunction-line will be five times $1\frac{3}{5}$ years, or 8 years, less the short interval corresponding to the Earth's motion over the arc E_5E. We see, then, how it comes to pass that an interval of eight years brings round nearly the same circumstances as at the beginning of the interval, and why, therefore, when a transit has occurred, another may occur eight years later. . . .

" And now let us consider the effect of the inclination of the orbit of Venus to that of the Earth, still, for the sake of simplicity, leaving out of account the slight eccentricity of the orbits.

" If EE', VV' (Figure 25), represent the two orbits,[1] and Æ be the place of the Earth at the autumnal equinox, then the line EE' represents the intersection of the two orbit-planes; and if, as before, we regard the plane of the paper as containing the orbit EE', then the part V'vV of the path of Venus is to be regarded as slightly above, the part Vv'V' as slightly below, the plane of the paper. Accordingly the end of the pointer which we have supposed Venus to carry round the Sun, passes above the semi-circle E'eE and below the semi-circle Ee'E'. And supposing this pointer to be of the length SE, so that its end appreciably travels round Ee'E'e (except for the displacement below and above the plane of this

---

[1] In the description of Figure 25 I have altered slightly Proctor's lettering so as to correspond with the use I shall make of the reasoning later on. Proctor starts with the transit of 1631 while I begin with that of 1761.

orbit), it is easy to calculate how much above or below the level Ee′E′e the end of the pointer runs. When in the direction SE or SE′, of course the Venus-carried pointer has its extremity on the Earth's path; when in direction Sve or Sv′e′, at right angles to EE′, the end of the pointer is at its farthest from

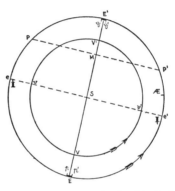

FIGURE 25.   The transit regions (pp′ and qq′) in the Earth's orbit.

the plane Ee′E′e. The inclination of the orbit of Venus being about 3° 23½′, and the distance Se (the Earth's distance from the Sun) being about 91,430,000 miles,[1] it is easily calculated that the extremity of the pointer passes above *e* and below *e′* at a distance of about 5,409,000 miles. At any other point as P or P′, the end is above or below by an amount less than 5,409,000 miles in the same degree that PM or P′M is less than eS, or e′S (PMP′ being drawn square to EE′)."

[1] Proctor's work, *Transits of Venus*, was published in 1875. Since that date the mean distance of the Earth from the Sun has been ascertained to be about 92,900,000 miles. The difference between Proctor's figures and the real distance affects the accuracy of his subsequent calculations.

By means of this theorem Proctor computes that the length of the transit regions pp', qq' is about 3° 28'.

Figure 26 will facilitate the discussion of the eight-year cycle of Venus in its relation to the Earth and the Sun. In 1761 and in 1769 there were June transits of Venus and in 1874 and 1882 there were December transits. Let us assume that at the 1761 transit the Earth and Venus stood in their orbits at the points E and V. Then according to the reasoning which has just been traversed the next inferior conjunctions of Venus and the Earth were at E_1V_1, E_2V_2, E_3V_3, E_4V_4, E_5V_5. The conjunction at E_5V_5 was just 2° 22' behind the point at which Venus and the Earth stood eight years before, and as E_5 fell within the transit region there was a June transit in 1769. Now just as the fifth conjunction E_5 was 2° 22' behind E, so the sixth conjunction occurred 2° 22' behind E_1; the seventh, 2° 22' behind E_2; the eighth, 2° 22' behind E_3; the ninth, 2° 22' behind E_4; and the tenth, 2° 22' behind E_5. In case of all five of the conjunction regions, there were inferior conjunctions 2° 22' behind the points of conjunction which occurred eight years previously. The sequence is followed out in Figure 26 to the 81st conjunction.

If now we consider the two transit regions pp', qq', we observe that the recession of the conjunction lines at the rate of 2° 22' in eight years caused the conjunctions in the region VE to recede from the transit region pp', and those in the region V_1E_1 to approach the transit region qq'. The distance of E_1 from E is about $215\frac{1}{2}°$ and the distance of the transit region qq' from the transit region pp' is 180°. As the transit region is

itself about 3° 28′, it is obvious that the distance of E_1
from the transit region is about 34°; and as the conjunctions in the region E_1 approach the transit region qq′ at
the rate of 2° 22′ every eight years while the conjunctions in the region pp′ recede at the rate of 2° 22′ every

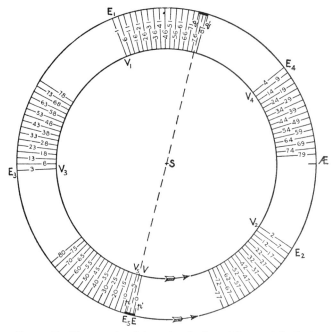

FIGURE 26.   The regression of the conjunction lines of Venus and the Earth.

eight years, it is clear that a conjunction must occur
within 17° of either the pp′ or the qq′ transit region
every eight years.   It is this eight-yearly conjunction
in the neighborhood of the transit regions which is synchronous with the eight-yearly terrestrial phenomena
that we have already described.   This eight-yearly cycle
is the Venus cycle for which we have been in search.

Up to this point no account has been taken of the small eccentricities in the orbits of the Earth and Venus and of the unequal motions of the planets in the different parts of their orbits. The consequences of these facts are so well known that they have been calculated,[1] and it is sufficient for our purpose to observe that the eight-year sequence in the transit regions—the Venus cycle—still persists when the eccentricities of the orbits and the varying motions of the planets are taken into consideration.

We see, therefore, that in 1761 and again in 1769 the Earth, Venus, and the Sun were in a straight line in the transit region pp' ; they were again in a straight line in 1874 and 1882 in the transit region qq'. Between the limiting dates 1761 and 1882, at intervals of approximately eight years, the Earth, Venus, and the Sun, in this sequence, made their nearest approach to being in a straight line. After 1882 until the date of the next transit in 2004, the Earth, Venus and the Sun will make this maximum approach to a straight line, in this sequence, at intervals of approximately eight years.

Now the longest record we have of economic cycles is given in Figure 20, which is the record of the crops in England. That invaluable sequence runs from 1760 to 1914. The maxima of the crop cycles occurred at 1762 and at intervals of eight years thereafter. The Venus cycle had maxima in June, 1761, and approximately eight years thereafter, so that at intervals of eight years before and after the dates of the last transits in December, 1874, and 1882, the maxima of the economic, meteorological, and Venus cycles were congruent.

[1] Proctor, *Transits of Venus*, pp. 111–118.

We come now to the second part of our question: is there reason for believing that the Venus cycle is accompanied with a synchronously varying force which could produce the observed meteorological cycles? Here our point of departure is a comparatively recent discovery of great importance relating to the period of rotation of Venus upon its axis.

From the observations of some faint markings supposedly on the surface of Venus, Domenico Cassini of Bologna in 1666–67 inferred that the period of rotation was about twenty-three hours. J. J. Cassini, in 1740, gave a more exact estimate of twenty-three hours and twenty minutes. Schroeter, in 1789, fixed the period at twenty-three hours and twenty-one minutes, and De Vico, in 1839–41, carried the spurious accuracy to twenty-three hours, twenty-one minutes, and twenty-two seconds. So the matter remained until 1890, when Schiaparelli announced his surprising discovery.

Schiaparelli made the innovation of conducting his observations by day, as near to noon as possible, when Venus would be highest and its own glare reduced by the brilliant midday sky. From a long series of careful observations he concluded that the period of rotation of Venus upon its axis could be nothing like twenty-four hours, but must lie between six and nine months and very probably agreed exactly with its period of revolution around the Sun, which is, approximately, 225 days.

In 1896 the question was made the subject of research by Percival Lowell with the assistance of an accomplished staff, at his observatory in the clear air of Flagstaff, Arizona. The markings noted by Schiaparelli upon which he based his conclusions as to the long period of rotation were verified at the Lowell Observatory, and in addition new markings were discovered and photographed. "By watching them assiduously it was possible to note that no change in position occurred in them, first through an interval of five hours, then through one of days, then of weeks. Care was taken to guard against illusion. It thus became evident that they bore always the same relation to the illuminated portion of the disk. This illuminated part, then, never changed. In other words, the planet turned always the same face to the Sun. The fact lay beyond a doubt, though of course not beyond a doubter." [1] Thirteen years after these first discoveries Professor Lowell repeated, in 1909, the account of his early work and then said "the years that have passed since these observations were made have brought corroboration of them. Several observers at Flagstaff have seen and drawn them and added discoveries of their own." [2]

The conclusion that the period of rotation of Venus upon its axis is the same as its period of revolution around the Sun was reached by Schiaparelli and Lowell from telescopic observations. There was, of course, the possibility, though not the probability, that both observers had been misled by visual errors. But no such deception could occur with the spectroscope, and to make sure of his ground Lowell installed at his observatory a spectroscopic equiqment. The investigator was Dr. Slipher, the present Director of the Lowell Observatory. The accuracy with which Dr. Slipher could de-

---

[1] Percival Lowell, *The Evolution of World*, pp. 77-79.
[2] *Ibid.*, p. 79.

termine the rotation period of a planet by means of
spectrograms was tested by his spectroscopic approxi-
mation of the well known periods of rotation of Mars
and Jupiter. The rotation period of Mars is known to
be $24^h 37^m 23^s.66$. Dr. Slipher determined its period
from spectrograms within an hour of the true time. The
rotation period of Jupiter is $9^h 50^m.4$. Dr. Slipher found
the rotation period from spectrograms to be $9^h 50^m$, or
within a minute of the exact time. When, in an exactly
similar manner, he made his observation of Venus, the
spectrograms showed that the rotation period must
exceed three months, which meant that so slow a rotation as three months was beyond the power of Dr.
Slipher's spectroscope to disclose.[1]

[1] Lowell, *The Evolution of Worlds*, pp. 83–89.

The reasoning of the next chapter will show that the theory of
perturbation by Venus will stand even if the period of the planet's
rotation on its axis is not coincident with the period of revolution about
the Sun. Nevertheless I wish to add opinions of experts confirmatory
of the statement in the text:

(a) "Dr. W. W. Campbell, Director of the *Lick Observatory* . . .
states: 'We have given some attention to the spectrographic velocities
of the east and west edges of the planet Venus, but we have written
very little on the subject. Our results seem to point to a long period
of rotation; at least several days in length and possibly a period coincident with the revolution period around the Sun.' " *Popular Astronomy*, March, 1922, p. 139.

(b) "It may be remarked that when the observations are corrected
for the systematic displacements to the violet discussed above, the
difference between morning and evening series, viewed in the light of the
probable error of observations, is not of an order that would indicate
a divergence from the assumed parallax or a rate of rotation higher
than that found by Slipher." "On Systematic Displacement of Lines
in Spectra of Venus." By Charles E. St. John and Seth B. Nicholson.
Contribution from the Mount Wilson Observatory, No. 208, p. 9.

(c) "By the use of Barnet 'Ultra Rapid' plates hypersensitised
with ammonia it has been possible to photograph Venus spectra with
a very narrow slit, and these are the finest plates hitherto obtained.
They give no evidence of an inclination of the lines due to a rotation

Lowell regarded Dr. Slipher's spectrogram report as confirmatory of Schiaparelli's conclusion and his own that Venus rotates on its axis in the same time that it revolves around the Sun, turning always the same side to the source of light and heat.

The bearing of this discovery upon the theory of the effect of Venus upon terrestrial meteorological cycles we shall approach by considering the following quotation from Lowell: "That Venus turns on her axis in the same time that she revolves about the Sun, in consequence of which she turns always the same face to him, must cause a state of things of which we can form but faint conception, from any earthly analogy. One face baked for countless aeons, and still baking, backed by one chilled by everlasting night, while both are still surrounded by air, must produce indraughts from the cold to the hot side of tremendous power. A funnel-like rise must take place in the centre of the illuminated hemisphere, and the partial vacuum thus formed would be filled by air drawn from its periphery which, in its turn, would draw from the regions of the night side. Such winds would sweep the surface as they entered, becoming less superficial as they advanced, and the marks of their inrush might well be discernible even at the distance we are off." [1]

The last part of this quotation is perhaps hyperbole. I am very far from wishing to suggest that the winds of Venus may be directly responsible for the periodicity in terrestrial weather. Our question is this: is there

of the planet when the terminator is placed normal to the slit." *Annual Report of the Director of Kodaikanal and Madras Observatories* for 1920, p. 2.

[1] *The Evolution of Worlds*, pp. 80–82.

reason for believing that the Venus cycle is accompanied with a synchronously varying force which could produce the terrestrial meteorological cycles? The consequence of the long rotation period of Venus with the one face always turned towards the Sun is that the planet is in a constant state of violent meteorological commotion on a vast scale; and this planet, which is about the size of the Earth, thrusts itself at intervals of eight years almost exactly in the direct path of radiation from the Sun to the Earth. Is it not probable that the storm-racked planet creates a disturbance in the interplanetary medium which affects the Sun's radiation on its way to the Earth? If that is the case, then the cause of the eight-year generating cycle is the planet Venus in its eight-yearly periodic motion with respect to the Earth and the Sun.

CHAPTER V

THE EIGHT-YEAR GENERATING CYCLE IN RELATION TO ITS PHYSICAL CAUSE

"You ask a rational question, and answering to the Objection, I say: That although Astronomy in the courses of many ages hath made a great progress in discovering the constitution and motions of the Celestial bodies, yet is it not hitherto arrived at that height, but that very many things remain undecided, and haply many others also undiscovered."

—GALILEO.

"Dans l'évolution du système du monde, les forces électriques et magnétiques semblent jouer un rôle comparable à celui de la force de gravitation."

—KR. BIRKELAND.

THE preceding chapter closed with the suggestion that the eight-yearly interposition of Venus between the Sun and the Earth may be responsible for the eight-year generating cycle. Reasons were given for assuming that Venus may be in a state of vast meteorological commotion, and the conjecture was offered that her interposition between the Sun and the Earth produces a disturbance in the interplanetary medium which affects the solar radiation on its way to the Earth.

When this theory was first advanced a distinguished man of science wrote me that the eight-year cycles appeared to be established but the alleged cause was "hard to digest" for the reason that one could not conceive how Venus might produce the effect. The criticism recalls the attitude of Galileo when he assailed the theory that the Moon might be responsible for certain terrestrial tides: "To say . . . that the motion of the Earth meeting with the motion of the Lunar Orb, the concurrence of them occasioneth the Ebbing and Flowing, is absolute vanity . . . because it is not exprest, nor seen how it should so happen. . . ."[1]

The object of the present chapter is to show how Venus may produce the cyclical effect. We shall approach the explanation by considering certain important recent discoveries in Solar Physics.

Recent Theories of the Sun

Solar Physics may be said to have had its beginning in 1610 when Galileo's discovery of sunspots introduced the idea of variability in the Sun. It became a science with clear-cut aims in consequence of the pertinacity of a German amateur, Herr Heinrich Schwabe of Dessau. Schwabe's discovery of the sunspot cycle not only has a direct bearing upon the theory of the Sun's activity, to which reference will be made later on, but falling as it does within the realm of the most exact of the sciences, its history cannot fail to give courage to economists engaged in the study of periodicities in notoriously inexact data.

Schwabe began his work in 1826. His observatory was a small apartment at the top of his dwelling and his instruments were two small telescopes with low powers. His method of observation is described[2]

---

[1] Galileo: *The Systeme of the World in Four Dialogues*   Translation by Thomas Salisbury, pp. 421–422.

[2] "Address delivered by the President, M. J. Johnson, Esq., on presenting the Medal of the Society to M. Schwabe." *Monthly Notices of the Royal Astronomical Society*, vol. xvii, pp. 126–132.

by his English contemporary, Mr. Manuel Johnson, President of the *Royal Astronomical Society:*

"His plan is to note by a number each spot in the order of its appearance, carrying on his notation from the first to the last spot in each year. He reckons an isolated spot or a cluster of spots where there is no visible separation between their penumbrae, as one group. 'Hence,' he observes, 'the number of spots will depend in a great measure on the excellence of the telescope; and it often happens that the clusters of many hundred, nay, of many thousand spots, will be designated by one number only, just as a single isolated spot will be. So great, however, is the Sun's tendency to present his spots in the form of clusters, that observers will in the course of a year, assuredly not find any great difference between their numbers and mine.' But he particularly impresses his reader that he attaches importance not so much on the absolute number of groups, as on the ratio which obtains between them in different years."

For ten years Schwabe's daily countings of the sunspots were published annually in the *Astronomische Nachrichten* apparently without attracting any attention. In 1838 he grouped his annual observations for the period 1826–1837 but forebore to indicate a periodicity, and his researches were still ignored by his fellow astronomers. For five more years he continued to publish his records annually when in 1843 he made the announcement of periodicity in his data.

But even then his work received no recognition. Not until 1851, when Alexander Humboldt mentioned in his *Cosmos* the discovery by Schwabe, did the theory of periodicity in sunspots receive the attention of professional astronomers. In 1857, the *Royal Astronomical Society* made official recognition of Schwabe's heroic courage, patience, and labor by bestowing upon him its highest honor.

In presenting the gold medal of the *Astronomical Society* to Herr Schwabe, President Johnson called attention to the discouraging atmosphere in which the discoverer entered upon his observations. The opinions of his predecessors who had studied the appearance of sunspots were apparently unanimous as to the lawlessness of their occurrence and as to the inutility of observing them. According to the astronomer Long, "Solar spots observe no regularity in their shape, magnitude, number, or in the time of their appearance or continuance." Lalande corroborated this opinion, "Les apparitions des taches du Soleil n'ont rien de regulier," and Delambre added the weight of his authority to the prevailing view. "Il est vrai qu'elles (sunspots) sont plus curieuses que vraiment utiles."

Mr. Johnson proceeded to characterize the discovery in these words:

"The result of his investigation . . . has been to establish with a degree of probability almost amounting to certainty, that the solar spots pass through the phases of maximum and minimum frequency, and *vice versa*, in a period not very different from ten years."

"Twelve years, as I have said, he spent to satisfy himself—six more to satisfy, and still thirteen more to

convince, mankind. For thirty years never has the
Sun exhibited his disk above the horizon of Dessau
without being confronted by Schwabe's imperturb-
able telescope, and that appears to have happened on
the average about 300 days a year. So, supposing that
he observed but once a day, he made 9000 observations,
in the course of which he discovered about 4700 groups.
This is, I believe, an instance of devoted persistence
unsurpassed in the annals of astronomy. The energy
of one man has revealed a phenomenon that had eluded
even the suspicion of astronomers for 200 years!"

Let us for a moment look more closely into Schwabe's
methods and results:

(1) Length of his observations. He began his observations in 1826 and announced in 1843 his discovery
of a periodicity of ten years. His observations of 18
years covered not quite two full periods of the phenomenon.

(2) Variability of the period. At the time Schwabe's
discovery received official recognition, February, 1857,
his observations covered just thirty years, or, assuming
the period to be ten years, the length of three cycles.
In the very act of praising his work President Johnson
was prompted to say, "the exact period Schwabe does
not pretend to have determined. That it is liable to
perturbation is evident. During twenty-seven years of
the series, the results were extremely regular; during
the last three years they have shown symptoms of
disturbance. The epoch of minimum which consistently
with earlier indications should have happened in 1853,
did not occur until 1856."

(3) Other coexistent cycles. As far as I am aware he

made no attempt to establish the existence of other cycles than the one of a supposed ten-year period.

(4) The cause of the cycle. The discoverer of the sunspot cycle did not advance a theory as to the cause of the cycle. For this statement we have the authority of the President of the *Astronomical Society:*

"Schwabe has not entered into speculation as to the nature and origin of sunspots."

(5) The method of measuring the length of the cycle. Schwabe was not embarrassed with three of the most difficult problems in the mathematical theory of cycles: the problem of distinguishing between real and spurious cycles; the problem of separating compound cycles into their constituent elements; and the problem of measuring the exact length of a cycle.

Nevertheless "the outcome of Schwabe's work was the first step in the whole series of discoveries which have gradually built up the modern science of Solar Physics." [1]

The first momentous consequence of Schwabe's discovery was the perception of an entirely new form of action by the Sun upon the Earth. Until Schwabe's time all theories of solar action proceeded upon the assumption that the Sun could affect the Earth in only three ways—through gravitation, through heat, or through light. But with the establishment of the cyclical variation of sunspots and with the accumulation of observations bearing upon the variations of the magnetic needle, it was a natural step to compare these two forms of oscillation. In 1852 Sir Edward Sabine

[1] H. H. Turner, *Astronomical Discovery*, p. 157, also p. 176.

announced the discovery of the synchronism between the sunspot cycles and the frequency of terrestrial magnetic storms. His findings were quickly confirmed by Wolf and Gautier, and subsequent observations have strengthened the theory of the essential concordance of the sunspot cycle and the cycles of terrestrial magnetic variations. But how can the Sun at a distance of 93 millions of miles affect the state of terrestrial magnetism? The investigations which have the solution of this problem in view are among the most stimulating of contemporary inquiries and, as will appear later on, they have a direct bearing upon our meteorological problem.

After one series of terrestrial phenomena had been shown to be in direct accord with the sunspot cycle, it was inevitable that a host of alert investigators should set about discovering other agreements. For some time it had been known that the aurora borealis and magnetic disturbances were associated phenomena, and about 1819 Arago had added materially to the measured evidence of their relation. With Sabine's proof of the synchronism of the sunspots and magnetic storms, it was only a corollary that the aurorae should vary with the sunspot cycle. To Wolf, of Zürich, credit is usually given for the detailed proof of the coincidence.

Economists are familiar with Sir William Herschel's speculation[1] in 1801 on the possible relation of sun-

[1] "Observations tending to investigate the Nature of the Sun, in order to find the Causes or Symptoms of its Variable Emission

spots to the crops through variations of the weather. He assumed that the variation in the number of the sunspots was probably accompanied with a variation in the amount of heat received upon the Earth which would be manifested in a quickened or blighted vegetation. Indeed, he made the first attempt, as far as I am aware, to establish a relation between changes in the number of sunspots and changes in the price of wheat. Necessarily his pioneer undertaking could be only suggestive because of the lack of data, but since Schwabe's time there has been unremitting effort to show correlation between the sunspots and changes in the terrestrial weather.[1]

W. S. Jevons, as every economist knows, attempted to work out the Herschel theory of the synchronism of sunspots and the yield of the crops. His heroic honesty in confessing his failure in his study of European data is not so commonly known. Assuming that the true length of the cycle in trade was eleven years— the true length of the principal sunspot cycle at the time of the publication of Jevons' essay had been shown to be approximately eleven years—Jevons arranged the prices of English crops during the 13th and 14th centuries in series of eleven years, and without making any statement as to whether the cycles of sunspots were congruent with the cycles of the crops, he advanced the theory of an eleven year cycle in the prices of farm

of Light and Heat; with Remarks on the Use that may possibly be drawn from solar Observations." *Philosophical Transactions of the Royal Society of London*, 1801, pp. 265 to 318. Particularly pp. 313–318.

[1] For a vast amount of data, see *The Computer's Handbook*, published by the English *Meteorological Office*, 1919.

crops, the cause of which is connected with the cause of
the eleven-year cycle of the sunspots. In a subsequent
essay he published this confession: [1]

"In 1875 I made a laborious reduction of the data
contained in Professor Thorold Rogers' admirable
*History of Agriculture and Prices in England from the
Year 1259*. I then believed that I had discovered the
solar period in the prices of corn and various agricultural commodities, and accordingly read a paper to
that effect at the *British Association* at Bristol. Subsequent inquiry, however, seemed to show that periods
of three, five, seven, nine, or even thirteen years would
agree with Professor Rogers' data just as well as a
period of eleven years; in disgust at this result I with-
drew the paper from further publication."

Influence of the New Physics

In the seventies of the last century the researches of
Sir William Crookes on the discharge of electricity
through gases initiated a course of inquiry which has
led to results that dominate both contemporary physics and contemporary astronomy. By improving devices for exhausting the contents of discharge tubes he
was able to obtain much nearer approaches to vacua
than had previously been possible and he was consequently able to conduct, under much more favorable
circumstances, experiments on the effects of electrical
discharges in rarefied media.

In Figure 27 there is an outline sketch of the simplest
type of discharge tube. Platinum wires to conduct

[1] *Investigations in Currency and Finance*, p. 225.

the electric current are sealed into the glass of the tube, forming electrodes at the points A and C. The end of the wire where the current enters the tube, A, is the anode, and the other end, C, where the current makes its exit is the cathode. The electrodes are usually tipped with some substance, such as aluminium, that

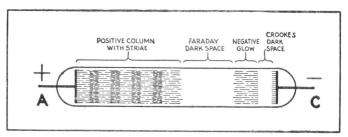

FIGURE 27.   A simple discharge tube.

does not easily volatilize under an electric discharge. The degree of vacuum that is obtained is measured by the pressure of the gas within the tube.

Under the conditions of ordinary pressure, air and other gases are among the best insulators of electricity. But when a highly rarefied gas is confined within a discharge tube and the electric tension between the electrodes is great, the gas becomes a conductor and reveals the remarkable phenomena that have led to the recent views as to the nature of electricity. If, for example, a tube with anode and cathode about twelve inches apart is filled with air at ordinary pressure, no spark will pass between the electrodes even when the tension is comparatively high. When, however, the pressure is reduced to about one millimetre of mercury, a glow appears at the two electrodes, the positive glow being greater than the glow at the cathode, and the space between the two glows remains dark.

When the gas is still further rarefied the glow near the cathode begins to change, leaving a light close to the cathode,—the cathode glow—which is separated by a dark space—the Crookes' dark space—from the other part of the original cathode light which is now called the negative glow. The relatively dark space between the negative glow and the glow at the anode is the Faraday dark space. The positive glow, or positive column, breaks up into a series of bright and dark striae at right angles to the line between the anode and the cathode. With still further reduction of the pressure of the gas the negative glow and the Crookes' dark space fill more and more of the tube, and the positive column correspondingly decreases. Streamers of bluish light, called cathode rays, are seen to start out perpendicularly from the cathode. If the exhaustion of the gas is carried still further the Crookes' dark space apparently fills the entire tube, and the walls of the tube become fluorescent, particularly where the cathode rays impinge, the color of the fluorescence varying according to the composition of the glass of the tube.

Crookes' researches were concerned primarily with the properties of the cathode light. The cathode rays apparently started perpendicularly from the cathode, producing fluorescence upon the walls of the tube where they impinged. His experiments led him to the conclusion that these streamers originated on the metal surface of the negative electrode and were a new manifestation of matter. He called it *radiant matter*. Many of his critics, most of whom were scandalized by his postulating a new form of matter, inferred from the luminescent effect of the rays that they must be some form of wave motion in the ether analogous to ultra-violet light.

The controversy as to the nature of the cathode rays lasted nearly twenty years until Sir J. J. Thomson, in 1895, following the lead of Perrin, proved that they are not ethereal waves but negatively electrified particles with definite mass. The experiments of Professor Thomson not only were conclusive with respect to the nature of the cathode rays but were suggestive of epoch-making views with regard to the theory of electricity and the constitution of the atom.

The characteristics of cathode rays which, for our purpose, should be specified are these:

(1) Cathode rays originate at the cathode of the discharge tube and proceed in straight lines perpendicular to the cathode. The rays will take this direction, normal from the cathode, no matter where the anode may be placed.

(2) They light up a fluorescent screen when they fall upon it.

(3) They are composed of negatively electrified particles.

(4) They may be deflected from their path by a magnetic or an electrostatic field.

   The experimental proof is suggested by the preceding characteristics. As the cathode rays light up a fluorescent screen the deflecti-bility of the rays by a magnet or by an electrically charged body may be observed, under proper conditions, by the movement of the light upon the screen when the rays are subjected to a magnetic or an electro-static influence.

The very great importance for our purpose of the magnetic and electric deflectibility of these rays will be pointed out later on.

(5) They ionize gases through which they pass and consequently render the gases conductors of electricity.

We have seen that cathode rays are com-posed of negatively charged particles which have recently been called electrons. The theory of ionization by the cathode rays is that the passage of the rays separates the gas into molecules which because of the activity of the rays have individually gained or lost one or more electrons. These mole-cules, which in this state are known as *gaseous ions*, become carriers of electric current.

(6) The gaseous ions produced by cathode rays may become nuclei for the condensation of water vapor.

Sir J. J. Thomson's treatise was not the only piece of epoch-making research that grew out of the investigation of cathode rays. In Germany, at the University of Würzburg, Professor Roentgen, in 1895, was at work upon the problem of cathode rays when he made the discovery of the rays, subsequently called X-rays or Roentgen rays, which were almost immediately put to spectacular as well as humane uses in the practice of medicine. The cathode rays had been observed to produce luminiscence when they impinged upon the walls of the Crookes' tube. Roentgen showed that the rays which he discovered originated at the point where the cathode rays collided with a solid substance. Later researches showed that X-rays are produced under the best circumstances when a definite surface to receive the cathode rays—the anti-cathode—is prepared of polished metals. The view which is at present generally accepted as to the nature of the X-rays was first advanced by Sir George Gabriel Stokes. He suggested that they are electro-magnetic waves having their origin in the oscillation of the electrical charge upon the cathode particle when the particle is brought to a sudden stop by striking a solid substance.

The principal characteristics of X-rays that we need to consider are these:

(1) The X-rays originate at the spot in which cathode rays strike a solid substance.
(2) They light up a fluorescent screen.
(3) They are not deflected in a magnetic field.
(4) They produce an ionization of gases through which they pass.
(5) The gaseous ions may become nuclei for the condensation of water vapor.

The cathode rays, as we have seen, are negatively charged particles moving normally from the cathode. If an obstacle, say a metal Maltese cross, is placed in the path of the cathode rays, two shadows of the cross will appear: one directly opposite the cathode on the wall of the tube and the other on the cathode itself. The shadow on the wall is explained by the intercepting of the cathode rays which would otherwise produce a fluorescence on the wall. The shadow on the cathode is due to the intercepting of positively charged molecules moving in the direction of the cathode. These are the positive or anode rays:

(1) The positive rays are positively charged molecules of the gas in the discharge tube streaming in the direction of the cathode.

(2) They light up a fluorescent screen.

(3) The size of the positively charged molecules is comparable with the size of the molecules of the gas, and they are much larger than the negatively charged particles in the cathode stream. The mass of the electrons is only about 1/1800th of that of a hydrogen atom, while its radius is only about 1/50,000th that of an atom.

(4) The positive rays are deflected both by a magnetic and an electrostatic field.

(5) They produce ionization of gases through which they pass.

(6) The gaseous ions may become nuclei for the condensation of water vapor.

There is a principle in physics known as the principle of reversibility which has been the means of a number of important discoveries. If a set of forces can produce an observed change, it is in order, according to the principle of reversibility, to inquire whether the converse relation may not hold true. If, for example, an electric current can produce a magnet, it is reasonable to suppose, as Faraday showed, that a magnet can produce an electric current. After the observation was made that cathode rays, positive rays, and Roentgen rays illuminate a fluorescent screen, the principle of reversibility obviously suggested that those substances which make good screens may possibly emit rays that are similar to the positive, cathode, and Roentgen rays.

Henri Becquerel was one of the first to enter this field which has been so successfully exploited by Professor and Madame Curie and Professor Rutherford. The history of researches into radio-activity is recent and well-known. The central discovery, however, needs to be connected with what has been said about the radiations attending the discharge of electricity in rarefied gases. Three principal kinds of rays, known respectively as α-, β-, and γ-rays, have been derived from radio-active substances, and these rays have their analogues in the radiations of the discharge tube. The α-rays are positively electrified and resemble in general characteristics the positive rays of the discharge tube. The β-rays are negatively electrified and resemble cathode rays. The γ-rays resemble the Roentgen rays.

These discoveries in electricity and in the nature of matter have produced a veritable renaissance in astronomical speculation. "La découverte des électrons et le succès croissant de la conception corpusculaire de l'électricité a . . . fait faire de grands progrès à nos connaissances sur le Soleil et celles-ci paraissent aujourd'hui, comme la Physique entière, dominées par cette nouvelle manière d'envisager les phénomènes." [1]

In the next section we shall give attention to some of these more recent astronomic theories in as far as they throw light upon changes in terrestrial meteorology which may be attributed to Venus. We shall, however, carry much more to the discussion if we bear in mind:

    (1) that nearly all forms of the rays we have considered are electrically charged and are deflectible by electric and magnetic fields;

    (2) that all of the rays produce ionization of gases;

    (3) that the gaseous ions may become nuclei for the condensation of water vapor.

Nearly half a century ago experiments by Coulier in France (1875) and by Aitken in Great Britain (1880–1881) revealed the importance of dust particles in the formation of clouds and the precipitaion of water vapor as rain. In their experiments upon air saturated with water vapor, clouds were formed, or not formed, under the same degree of saturation, according as dust was present or absent. The dust particles supplied the necessary nuclei for the condensation of the vapor.

The recent theory of ionization by radiation has added greatly to our knowledge of the process of cloud

[1] Bosler: "Sur les relations des orages magnétiques et des phénomènes solaires." *Annales de l'Observatoire d'Astronomie Physique de Paris,* Tome V, 1912, p. 7.

formation. Nuclei are essential, but they may be supplied, and are supplied, not only by dust particles but by the gaseous ions that result from the action of the many kinds of rays which have already been described. Indeed the objective existence of the gaseous ions was disputed by many physicists until their reality was placed beyond doubt by experiments in which precisely their capacity to act as nuclei for condensation of water vapor was employed to make their presence visible. C. T. R. Wilson, who devised the experiments, succeeded in obtaining actual photographs of rain-droplets formed about the ions along the tracks of the various types of rays discharging in vapor-saturated air.

Wilson's experiments on the ionization of gases and the condensation of water vapor were reported in 1911 and 1912. It was in the line of progress from his early conclusions to turn his attention to the problem of the relation of rainfall to electrical variations in the atmosphere. Accordingly we find this statement in the *Annual Report of the University of Cambridge* for 1919, in the section referring to the work of C. T. R. Wilson at the Solar Physics Observatory: [1]

"The results obtained in these investigations have suggested a theory which both accounts for many of the more important phenomena of thunderstorms, and relates them to those of fine weather atmospheric electricity and terrestrial magnetism." [2]

[1] Quoted by Bauer: "Some of the Chief Problems in Terrestrial Magnetism and Electricity," *Proceedings in the National Academy of Sciences*, 1920, vol. 6, pp. 575–576.

[2] There is an ample account of Wilson's researches upon this topic in a paper, "Investigations on Lightning Discharges and on the Electric

The Rôle of Venus

If Venus affects terrestrial weather it may obviously do so either directly through magnetic or electrostatic influence upon the Earth, or indirectly through magnetic or electrostatic influence[1] upon solar radiation on its way to the Earth. Both hypotheses imply that Venus is a seat of electrical activity. We shall first consider the evidence for this assumption.

Professor Hale, a resourceful and cautious investigator, has expressed the opinion "that every star, and probably every planet, is also a magnet, as the Earth has been known to be since the days of Gilbert's *De Magnete*," [2] and in 1921 Dr. Bauer, whose rare knowledge of contemporary thought is well known, has summarized in a sentence his view of the tendency of recent investigation: "That there are other bonds of union than those of gravitation—electrical in their nature—between the Earth, the sister planets, and our parent Sun, by means of which cosmic forces responsible for electric and magnetic effects are conveyed, is becoming increasingly evident." [3]

These authoritative opinions would probably justify

Field of Thunderstorms," *Philosophical Transactions of the Royal Society of London*, Series A, vol. 221, March, 1921, pp. 73–115.

[1] By the above statement I do not mean to limit to this kind of influence the possibility of disturbance by Venus. If, for example, Venus should be a source of radio-activity it could produce an effect upon the Earth directly through radiation and indirectly by altering the electric conductivity of the interplanetary medium.

[2] Hale, *The New Heavens*, p. 70.

[3] Bauer, "Measures of the Electric and Magnetic Activity of the Sun and the Earth, and Interrelations," *Terrestrial Magnetism and Atmospheric Electricity*, May and June, 1921, p. 42.

one in proceeding upon the hypothesis that Venus is a magnetic field, but it is well to add to them such direct observations as I have been able to find.

The first observation relates to the significance of a disturbance in the solar corona produced by the proximity of Venus.

As long ago as 1885 Sir William Huggins in his classical address before the *Royal Society*, "On the Corona of the Sun," defended the view that the corona is electrical in origin. A few years earlier, in 1881, Goldstein advanced the idea of the Sun's emitting cathode rays and even suggested that, perhaps, the key to the Sun's influence upon the electrical and magnetic phenomena of the Earth might be found in these negatively charged solar rays. The two conceptions were combined in an account of the solar corona by Deslandres. According to his theory the characteristic features of the solar corona are explained by assuming that the cosmical dust particles of the corona are each enveloped in a gaseous atmosphere rendered luminous by the phosphoresence produced by the cathode rays discharged from the Sun.

If now there is evidence that Venus produces a perturbation of the electrified solar corona, then the hypothesis which attributes to the planet a magnetic or electrical field becomes more worthy of being entertained. Sir William Huggins in the address to which reference has been made refers to the coronal perturbation by Venus:

"Hitherto in our discussion of the forces which may be active in the corona we have taken account only of the influence of electrical changes which take place upon the Sun. Now these changes at the Sun make themselves felt upon the Earth; we may then well suppose, with a high degree of probability, that the Earth, and especially the near planets Venus and Mercury exert an influence on the electrified and attenuated matter of the corona." "We know nothing of the electric distribution on Venus and Mercury, but it seems more than probable that these bodies as well as the meteor swarms nearer the Sun have an influence in determining the mode of out-flow of the electrified coronal matter in the direction in which they happen to be. The influence may be one of attraction, giving rise to coronal extension or rays from the corona, or to repulsion, in which case we might have what appears to us a rift directed towards the body.

"We have not sufficient data to furnish certain information on this point, but it may be of interest to quote the following sentence from Mr. Trouvelot's *Report of the Eclipse of 1878:*—'There is a fact connected with this eclipse, which, if not due to a singular coincidence, would seem to point to some attractive action of the planets on the solar atmosphere (corona). On the day of the eclipse Mercury and Venus were in almost opposite points of their orbits, with the Sun between them and almost on a line with them, while the Earth on the same day was in a part of its orbit which formed the apex of an equilateral triangle having for base the line joining Mercury and Venus. Knowing this, it is perhaps singular, and anyhow very remarkable, to see that the eastern wing of the corona was directed on a straight line to Mercury, while the western appendage was directed on a straight line to Venus. The coincidence was still greater. As in regard to the Sun, the two planets were not exactly on the same line, Mercury being a little to the North while Venus was a little to the South of the ecliptic, the solar appendages have shown the same peculiarity, their axes being a little inclined to each other. I may say that the inclination of the axes of the coronal extensions on the sides of the Sun may be seen in the photographs of the eclipse. It should be stated that Professor Newcomb, who observed the coronal extension towards Venus says, 'I tried to judge whether the western one (ray) pointed towards the planet Venus then plainly visible near the horizon. The direction was apparently very slightly below the planet.' Professor Newcomb's words seem to show that he did not make allowance for refraction, which would make the planet when near the horizon appear sensibly higher than its true place." [1]

The second observation supporting the hypothesis that Venus is a magnetic field relates to the significance of the disturbance of a comet by the proximity of Venus. Here, as in the case of the solar corona, the increasing knowledge of electrical forces has supplied fruitful hypotheses where hitherto little progress had

[1] The Bakerian Lecture.—"On the Corona of the Sun," by Sir William Huggins, D. C. L., L. L. D., F. R. S. *Proceedings of the Royal Society of London*, vol. xxxix, 1885, pp. 130, 131.

been made in understanding the phenomena. A corollary of Maxwell's electro-magnetic theory of light was that light must exert pressure. The idea was seized upon by Arrhenius as a clue to the explanation of comets' tails. He assumed that negatively charged small bodies are driven off from the Sun under the influence of light-pressure, and are electrically discharged in the gases surrounding the comet thereby causing the characteristic shape and glow of the comet's tail.[1]

Birkeland, in his theory of comets' tails, substituted cathode rays or streams of electrons for Arrhenius' negatively charged small bodies.[2] Deslandres, Bernard, and Bosler rendered still more probable the hypothesis of the cathode rays by their spectroscopic studies of Morehouse's comet in 1908, in which they showed the resemblance of the comet's radiation to that of cathode rays in a Crookes' tube.[3]

[1] "Eine andere Schwierigkeit bieten die Gase der Kometen insofern, als sie leuchten, wenn sie in einer Entfernung von der Sonne sind, wo die Temperatur nicht wohl höher sein kann als auf dem heissesten Punkte des Mondes. Dies zeigt, dass wahrscheinlicherweise elektrische Vorgänge hier vor sich gehen. Dies kann durch die Theorie erklärt werden, wenn man annimmt, dass von der Sonne nach allen Seiten negativ geladene kleine Körper ausgestrahlt werden. Diese treffen den Kometen und bewirken da Entladungen, welche die Gase zum Glühen bringen. Arrhenius, *Lehrbuch der Kosmischen Physik*, 1903, p. 204.

[2] "Arrhenius has also, as we know, maintained a similar theory, only that instead of electric corpuscle-rays of the kind here considered, he imagines rays of electrically-charged atoms, moving under the influence of light-pressure." Birkeland, *The Norwegian Aurora Polaris Expedition*, 1902–1903, p. 631.

[3] "Dans un ordre d'idées bien différent, mais également en faveur de la théorie cathodique, on peut encore relever un fait intéressant: le spectre de la queue de certaines comètes, et plus particulièrement de la comète Morehouse (1908 c), s'est montré identique à celui que

Now whether one accepts the theory of Arrhenius, or of Birkeland, or of Deslandres the tails of comets are electrical in nature and should show a distortion in the presence of a magnetic or an electric field. The following incident, therefore, has a bearing upon the hypothesis as to the magnetic field of Venus: In 1910 when Halley's "comet passed near Venus . . . the tail . . . broke up, as if a result of the near approach to the planet." [1]

The observations of Halley's Comet in 1910 throw light upon another aspect of our problem. Venus, according to the Director of the *Lowell Observatory*, seemed to break up the tail of the comet when the comet approached the planet. If now it can be shown that the comet in its approach to the Earth affected terrestrial meteorological conditions, there would seem to follow two probable conclusions: (1) that terrestrial weather is affected by the electro-magnetic condition of neighboring celestial bodies; and, (2) that Venus by influencing the magnetic field between neighboring bodies and the Earth may affect the Earth's weather. Two observations will be cited. The first is from Kr. Birkeland, the Norwegian physicist: Je mentionnerai . . . quelques observations faites le printemps dernier à mon observatoire, sur le pic de Halde, près de Bossekof, au moment du passage de la comète de Halley. On constata qu'après de violents orages magnétiques, il

certains gas présentent sous l'action du rayonnement cathodique." Bosler: "Sur les relations des orages magnétiques et des phénomènes solaires." *Annales de l'Observatoire d'Astronomie Physique de Paris,* 1912, pp. 8–9.

[1] V. M. Slipher, "The Spectrum of Halley's Comet in 1910 as Observed at Lowell Observatory," *Lowell Observatory Bulletin,* No. 52, p. 15.

pouvait produire une forte ionisation de l'atmosphère, de telle sorte que la conductibilité spécifique électrique de celle-ci était à certains moments 200 fois plus grande que la normale. L'atmosphère, au sommet de la montagne, avait une conductibilité telle qu'on aurait pu croire qu'il y avait du radium dans la voisinage des appareils.

Nous nous trouvons ici en face d'une découverte sans doute très importante, car on a ainsi trouvé une liaison électrique entre les phénomènes magnétiques de la terre et les phénomènes météorologiques. L'ionisation prononcée de l'atmosphère influe en effet sur la formation des nuages et sur l'état électrique de la terre." [1]

The next fact is taken from an address given in Leipzig by Augusto Rhigi, of Bologna.

Referring to the work of his assistants in the observations in Bologna, at the passage of Halley's comet, Rhigi says: "Die Herren, die in jener Nacht in meinem Institute Wache hielten, um die verschiedenen Messungen auszuführen, konnten ferner eine Kondensation von Wasserdampf von ungewöhnlicher Menge feststellen, die sich aus der Gegenwart vieler Ionen, und besonders negativer Ionen, erklären lässt." [2]

We have thus far considered the influence of Venus upon the solar corona and upon the tail of Halley's comet as tending to establish the hypothesis that

---

[1] Kr. Birkeland, "Orages magnétiques et aurores polaires," *Archives des sciences physiques et naturelles de Genève.* Quatrième periode, t. xxxii—Août, 1911.

[2] Augusto Rhigi, *Kometen und Elektronen*, Leipzig, 1911. Akademische Verlagsgesellschaft M. B. H., p. 60.

Venus is a magnetic or an electric field. Our next piece of evidence strengthens this hypothesis and at the same time increases the probability of a direct electro-magnetic action of Venus upon the Earth.

In 1911 Professor Arthur Schuster published a paper on "The Influence of Planets on the Formation of Sun-Spots." [1] Assuming that whatever planetary influence might exist, Jupiter, Venus, and Mercury would be likely to be most efficient, he sought to discover whether the formation of sunspots was in any way dependent upon the position of these planets with respect to the Sun. He interpreted his results in the light of the theory of probability, seeking thereby to eliminate chance associations. Our interest centers in this conclusion, namely, "if we take each planet separately . . . it is seen that only in the case of Venus do the numbers help to establish a real connection." [2]

In the same year, 1911, F. J. M. Stratton, Assistant in Astrophysics, at *Cambridge Observatory*, dealt with the same problem in a paper "On Possible Phase-relations between the Planets and Sun-spot Phenomena." [3] Using a slightly different method and confining his study to Jupiter and Venus, he reviewed the work of Professor Schuster. He reached the general conclusion "that the case for planetary effects on sun-spot phenomena is 'not proven'" (p. 26). But there was a notable qualification: "A careful study of the detailed figures underlying the tables in this paper leaves the author

[1] *Proceedings of the Royal Society of London*, Series A, vol. 85, 1911, pp. 309–323.

[2] *Ibid.*, p. 317.

[3] *Monthly Notices of the Royal Astronomical Society*, vol. 72, pp. 9–26.

unable to support the theory of a real planetary effect. Only in the case of the 3 h. maximum for Venus . . . does the inequality continue strongly throughout the series of observations " (p. 14). Resorting to the theory of probability to determine whether this apparent effect of Venus is a real effect, he concluded: "In general practice a deviation from the mean of less than three times the standard deviation is regarded as ascribable to fluctuations of sampling " (p. 14). "The standard deviation for the Venus spot-birth is 9.7. A residual of 30 in the figures for 3 h. does, according to the above criterion, call for explanation. Dr. Schuster suggests a planetary effect. To the present writer the evidence seems so uncertain that he prefers to suspend judgment until more figures are available " (p. 15).

The net result, for our purpose, of Mr. Stratton's review of Professor Schuster's work is that he finds the same formal indication of an effect on the part of Venus. Professor Schuster, reasoning from probabilities, regards the effect as real while Mr. Stratton, admitting the very great probability in favor of a real effect, prefers to suspend judgment until more figures are available.

If the Venus effect is real, then there is need of explaining how it is produced. One of the theories advanced by Professor Schuster is that the solar perturbation may be due to an electrostatic influence on the part of the planets, and he assumed that the planetary electrostatic influence would hardly diminish more rapidly than according to the inverse third power of the distance from the Sun.

At this point Professor Schuster's argument respect-

ing planetary influence upon the Sun and his finding
with regard to the effect produced upon the Sun by
Venus touch very closely the fundamental theory that
Venus exerts an electro-magnetic influence upon the
Earth either directly, or indirectly, through its effect
upon solar radiation on the way to the Earth. The
distance of Venus from the Sun is to the distance of the
Earth from the Sun as .723 to 1.000. At the time
of inferior conjunction the distance, on the average, of
Venus from the Sun is to its distance from the Earth
as .723 is to .277. Consequently, if we assume with
Professor Schuster that the electrostatic influence di-
minishes with the inverse cube of the distance, then
at the time of inferior conjunction, the influence of
Venus upon the Earth should be nearly eighteen times
as great as its influence upon the Sun.

The evidence already submitted would seem to warrant the hypothesis that Venus is a seat of a magnetic
or an electric field.[1] Furthermore, Professor Schuster's
argument that Venus may produce an electrostatic
influence upon the Sun would seem to tell with even

---

[1] Reference may be made to an undertaking to estimate the direct
influence of the planets upon the declination of the magnetic needle.
According to Ernst Leyst, there is a measurable influence, and one of
his conclusions is that the degree of effect is dependent in each case upon
the distance of the planet from the Earth and its position with respect
to the Earth and the Sun. "Die Erdnähe der Planeten bewirkt also
ein Anwachsen der westlichen Declination und die grössere Entfernung
der Planeten von der Erde, zur Zeit der Conjunction der äusseren
Planeten und der oberen Conjunction der Venus bewirkt eine Abnahme
der westlichen Declination." ErnstLeyst: "Über den Magnetismus
der Planeten," *Repertorium für Meteorologie*, Bd. xvii, No. 1, St.
Petersburg, 1894, p. 20. Leyst's results have been criticised as being
inconclusive.

greater strength in favor of the direct action of Venus upon the atmosphere of the Earth. We shall now consider the possibility of an indirect effect of Venus through the perturbation of radiation from the Sun to the Earth.

Even before the discovery of electrons and the formulation of the corpuscular theory of electricity, the synchronism in the variations of the magnetic needle with the frequency of sunspots had caused many to hold to a direct electric or magnetic action of the Sun upon the Earth. But how could the action be achieved at the distance of ninety-three millions of miles? The mystery has not yet been cleared up, but the investigations looking to its solution, as is usual in such cases, have been most fruitful in other discoveries.

Laboratory experiments had already established that the propagation of electrons is facilitated by extreme rarification of gases; that very hot bodies give off electrons; that the electrons proceed normally from the cathode; and that the position of the anode does not affect the course of the cathode rays. It was therefore an almost obvious step to assume that the Sun, being intensely hot, gives off negatively charged particles that are gathered in by the planets along their respective magnetic lines of force.[1]

---

[1] As an illustration of the hypotheses to which this fructifying conception led we have in compact form Sir Oliver Lodge's speculations: "The Earth is in fact a target exposed to cathode rays, or rather to electrons, emitted by a hot body, viz., the Sun. The Sun is evidently intensely radio-active; and the result of its discharge of electrons into the approximate vacuum of its immediate neighborhood is not unlikely to be the appearance known as the corona. The gradual accumulation of negative electricity by the Earth is a natural consequence of this

One of the very first to take this step was the physicist, Kr. Birkeland, of Christiania, whose primary objectives were the cause of magnetic storms and the origin of terrestrial magnetism. Holding as a working hypothesis that magnetic storms are probably traceable to solar bombardment by means of electric corpuscles, he laid the foundation of his work in an elaborate collection of observations relating to the aurora borealis and simultaneous variations in the magnetic needle. By a very rare combination of experimental ingenuity and speculative fertility he extended his electrical theory of cosmical phenomena to the solar corona, the zodiacal light, comets' tails, and Saturn's rings. To throw new light upon his theories he spent a fortune in building observatories in the far north, equipping sailing vessels, and organizing scientific expeditions in which he personally suffered the contrasting hardships and dangers of life within the arctic circle and within the tropics, in the Soudan. Whatever may be the eventual estimate of his theories, his collection of material[1]

electron bombardment extending to greater distances across space, where no residual matter exists; and the fact that the torrent of particles constitutes an electric current of fair strength gives an easy explanation of one class of electric storms; these storms having long been known, by the method of concomitant variations, to be connected with sunspots and aurorae. The electric nuclei, when they form ions, would also serve as centers of condensation of atmospheric water vapour at high altitudes, and so be liable to affect the rainfall. Moreover, the fact that water vapour condenses more readily on negative than on positive ions, seems to furnish us with one explanation of atmospheric electricity; for a fall of rain would bring down with it a negative charge, and would leave the upper regions positively electrified with respect to the Earth's surface: and this agrees with the known sign of the normal field of electric force in the atmosphere." Lodge, *Electrons or the Nature and Properties of Negative Electricity*, pp. 168–169.

[1] *The Norwegian Aurora Polaris Expedition*, 1902–1903.

will be of incalculable value in the solution of the problems that interested him, and the contemplation of his courage in thought and expression and his devotion to science will always produce an emotional elevation.

In the theories of Birkeland cathode rays, or β-rays, play an important rôle. It is to these negative particles which are shot off by the Sun and gathered in by the Earth along its magnetic lines of force that he attributed the aurora borealis and the simultaneous variations in the magnetic needle. For a while Birkeland's theory stood a chance of wide acceptance, but doubt was created by the dissent of his pupil Vegard and his mathematical colleague Carl Störmer both of whom had at first accepted his explanations but later attributed the phenomena to α-particles. He was fortunate, however, in the character of the men who opposed him, and in view of what has just been said about Birkeland's personality, his love for science and his unswerving fidelity in its pursuit, one cannot fail to have a lively satisfaction in the most recent utterance of his critics. Both Vegard and Störmer have modified their dissenting views and have taken a position much nearer Birkeland's original hypothesis:

"Dans son dernier ouvrage publié pendant la rédaction définitive du présent mémoire, *M. Vegard a abandonné sa théorie, que les aurores sont causées par des rayons a*; en effet, en étudiant la distribution de la lumière le long des rayons auroraux, il arrive à la conclusion que cette distribution ne peut pas être expliqué par sa théorie; il faut supposer que l'aurore est causée par des rayons cathodiques, des rayons β ou bien

par des rayons positifs très déviables par le ma-
gnétisme." [1]

Vegard then, according to Störmer, not only abandons
his own view but leans toward the Birkeland theory
which attributes the phenomena to the negatively
charged rays.

As for himself, Störmer says:

> "De la discussion . . . dans le *Terrestrial Magne-*
> *tism,* je tirai . . . la conclusion suivante: ' il semble
> comme démontré que l'aurore était due à des cor-
> puscles chargés d'électricité positive.' MM. Kr.
> Birkeland et Vegard ont critiqué cette conclusion,
> et le plus prudent sera probablement de ne pas pren-
> dre une résolution définitive avant d'avoir à dis-
> position une série de pareilles observations.   En
> effet, on ne sait pas encore le rôle exact joué dans un
> pareil phénomène par des courants terrestres ou par
> des courants corpusculaires en dehors de l'atmo-
> sphère." [2]

But we have seen that whether the rays be negative
or positive, α-rays or β-rays, they are deflectible by
either an electrostatic or a magnetic field.   Furthermore, as we have learned, C. T. R. Wilson has proved
experimentally that the gaseous ions produced by ionizing radiation may become nuclei for the condensation of
water vapor and has suggested that important phenomena of thunderstorms may be related to variations

[1] Carl Störmer, *Rapport sur une expédition d'aurores boréales à Bossekop
et Store Korsnes pendant le printemps de l'année 1913.*   Kristiania, 1921,
p. 158.

[2] *Ibid.,* p. 64.

in atmospheric electricity. Birkeland also, as I have remarked in the account of Halley's comet, attempted to connect meteorological phenomena with variations in the supply of ionizing cathode rays. It would seem obvious, therefore, that if Venus is the source either of a magnetic or an electrostatic field, its approach to, and recession from, the line of radiation from the Sun to the Earth and its interposition in the direct line of radiation must produce disturbances in terrestrial meteorology. If that be true, then, since the conjunctions of the Sun, Venus, and the Earth are periodically reproduced, meteorological disturbances should tend to show the same recurrent cycles.

The reasons for assuming that Venus may be the seat of a magnetic field have already been given. Likewise the proofs of the deflectibility of the ionizing rays have been reported. Supposing that Venus carries a magnetic field comparable in intensity with that of the Earth, what ground is there for believing that the trajectories of the corpuscles shot from the Sun would be so altered by the magnetic field of Venus as to affect materially the electric phenomena of the Earth? Fortunately we have the very best authority for making a positive statement.

After Birkeland advanced his hypothesis that the aurora borealis is due to cathode rays emanating from the Sun and taking a course in the Earth's atmosphere that is determined by terrestrial magnetic lines of force, Störmer undertook to subject the theory to a mathematical treatment. His primary problem was to devise mathematical ways of computing the probable trajectories of the electric corpuscles starting from the Sun and approaching the magnetic field of the Earth. It can readily be understood that the mathematical problem was difficult to formulate and the arithmetical computations were extremely laborious. As is usual in complicated mathematical problems, Störmer was compelled to proceed by first simplifying his hypothesis and then adding, one by one, the actual complicating circumstances. His first assumption ignored the perturbations due to the magnetic fields of the inner planets Mercury and Venus, which perturbations would of course vary not only with the strength of the respective magnetic fields of the planets, but also with their relative positions and velocities with respect to the Sun and the Earth. From the nature of his equations Störmer came to a conclusion of critical importance in the theory of the influence of Venus upon the radiation of the Sun to the Earth: "The trajectories . . . give a good idea of what enormous perturbations the planets Mercury and Venus will have on the movement of the electric corpuscles from the Sun to the Earth, if these planets are surrounded by a magnetic field of about the same strength as the magnetic field of the Earth." [1]

Thus far the argument has tended to show reason for believing the periodic configurations of the Sun, Venus, and the Earth to be a periodic source of terrestrial meteorological cycles. The criticism may be made with some fairness that if such an effect exists it should have been observed by scientists long ago. The reply to the criticism would take this form:

[1] Carl Störmer: "On the trajectories of electric corpuscles in space under the influence of terrestrial magnetism, applied to the aurora borealis and to magnetic disturbances." *Archiv för Mathematik og Naturvidenskab*, B. XXVIII, nr. 2, p. 35.

(1) The significance of the newer theories of electricity as a means of explaining the mode of action of the Sun upon the Earth is only beginning to be realized.

As an indication of progress I should note, in addition to what has already been said, the new view as to the nature of the interplanetary medium. In 1896 when J. J. Thomson and Roentgen were extending the researches of Crookes, Schuster raised the important question as to whether the interplanetary medium could transmit an electric current:

"Speculative theories on the magnetic and electric relationship between the Sun and Earth lack all solid basis until we can give an answer to the question, whether interplanetary space is to be considered an electric conductor or not." [1]

A quarter of a century later, in 1921, Dr. Bauer could make this reply: " . . . the evidences are getting stronger and stronger that interplanetary space, as the result of solar radiations and emanations, may indeed be an electric conductor, the possibility of which Schuster suggested." [2]

(2) Even now there is no adequate provision for the observations of the essential phenomena.

[1] *Terrestrial Magnetism*, vol. 1, 1896. Quoted by Dr. Bauer: "Measures of the Electric and Magnetic Activity of the Sun and the Earth, and Interrelations."
Terrestrial Magnetism, March and June, 1921, p. 37.
[2] Bauer, *Ibid.*, p. 38.

For example, it seems almost incredible that there should be no wide systematic observation of such an important known electrical effect as earth-currents. "As far as known, there has been but one observatory in recent years where systematic earth-current observations have been made, namely, at the *Observatio del Ebro*, Tortosa, Spain, where a very valuable series has been obtained from 1910–1920." Dr. Bauer, from whom this quotation is made, was compelled to add, "unfortunately the series was interrupted on January 1, 1921, because of defective earth-plates; it is much hoped that the defects will soon be remedied and the series continued." [1]

(3) The subject has been placed under a kind of scientific taboo. It has been regarded as the special domain of charlatans and astrologers.

The biographer of Sir Isaac Newton, Sir David Brewster, illustrates the complacent assurance, if not the arrogance, of an influential school of writers. Kepler had said, "I have seen the state of the atmosphere almost uniformly disturbed as often as the planets are in conjunction, and in the other configurations so celebrated among astrologers.

[1] Bauer: "Some Results of Recent Earth-Current Observations and Relations with Solar Activity, Terrestrial Magnetism, and Atmospheric Electricity." *Terrestrial Magnetism and Atmospheric Electricity*, March and June, 1922, p. 2 and p. 2 note 3.

I have noticed its tranquil state either when there are none or few such aspects, or when they are transitory and of short duration." The comment by Brewster, who died in 1868, mirrored the view of his contemporaries: "Had Kepler been able to examine these hasty and erroneous deductions by long-continued observation, he would soon have found that the coincidence which he did observe was merely accidental, and he would have cheerfully acknowledged it. Speculations of this kind, however, are from their very nature, less subject to a rigorous scrutiny; and a long series of observations is necessary either to establish or to overturn them. The industry of modern observers has now supplied the defect, and there is no point in science more certain than that the Sun, Moon, and planets do not exercise any influence on the general state of our atmosphere." [1]

(4) At least one competent astronomer has had the courage to enter the field, and in a singular manner his results bear out the thesis of this chapter as to the influence of Venus.

In July, 1922, a friendly astronomer gave me the following reference, A. Nodon: *Essai d'Astrométéorologie*, and I received from France a copy of the work in October, 1922. There is a *Préface* by M. G. Bigourdan,

[1] Sir David Brewster, *Martyrs of Science*, pp. 241–242.

Membre de l' Institut et du Bureau de Longitudes, in which he says "Cet essai d'*Astrométéorologie, et de ses applications à la prévision du temps, intéressera donc tous ceux qui, de près ou de loin, s'occupent de Météorologie. Il peut même présenter une véritable valeur pratique, et constituer une conception féconde pour l'avenir. Aussi l'Auteur mérite de vifs remercîments pour ses persévérantes recherches, qui doivent apporter à la Météorologie une aide efficace."* [1]

The extremely important quotation that I am about to make is a summary of his results, and its singularity consists not only in its neat confirmation of what has been said as to the influence of Venus, but in these facts —that of all the planets he considered, Venus alone

---

[1] M. Nodon's professional accomplishments and associations are indicated in the title-page description of his work:

Essai
D'Astrométéorologie
et ses applications
à la
prévision du temps
par
Albert Nodon
Officier de l'Instruction publique
Docteur ès Sciences
Ingenieur-Chimiste
Ex-adjoint à l'Observatoire d'Astronomie
physique de Paris
Membre correspondant de l'Académie royale des
Sciences de Barcelone
Président de la Société astronomique de Bordeaux.

The book was published in 1920, in Paris, by Gauthier-Villars et Cie.

should be particularly specified in his results; and of all possible configurations with respect to the Sun and the Earth, the period of approach to, and recession from, conjunction should be singled out as being of most importance.

"Une étude comparative des divers tableaux que nous avons précédemment passés en revue, fait apparaître des liens étroits entre les troubles solaires, les grandes perturbations de l'atmosphère, les troubles électriques et magnétiques, les dépressions générales, les sismes, la direction des vents, la pluie, le mauvais temps et le beau temps, dans les divers points du globe. Notre attention a été d'autre part, attirée par les actions dépendantes des positions relatives des *planètes* inférieures par rapport au Soleil, en particulier pendant les quadratures héliocentriques de la Terre et de Vénus. Ces actions paraissent être accrues pendant les époques de syzygies."

"Bref, il semble exister une étrange concordance entre la résultante des quadratures héliocentrique ☿ ♀, le nombre des centres actifs du soleil, les cyclones, les ondes de dépression et les sismes! Cette concordance est-elle fortuite, ou bien résulte-t-elle de cause à effet?" [1]

[1] Nodon: *Essai D'Astrométéorologie*, pp. 57, 172.

Also published in

Reprints Of Economic Classics

By Henry Ludwell Moore

Economic Cycles: Their Law and Cause

By HENRY LUDWELL MOORE

Professor of Political Economy in Columbia University

8vo, $2.00

Extract from the Introduction: "There is a considerable unanimity of opinion among experts that, from the purely economic point of view, the most general and characteristic phenomenon of a changing society is the ebb and flow of economic life, the alternation of energetic, buoyant activity with a spiritless, depressed and uncertain drifting. . . . What is the cause of this alternation of periods of activity and depression? What is its law? These are the fundamental problems of economic dynamics the solution of which is offered in this Essay."

Comments of Specialists

Moore's book is so important that it is sure to be widely criticized. . . . Yet so far as the fundamental conclusions are concerned the book is so firmly grounded on a vast body of facts that its main line of argument seems unassailable. . . . Moore has gone much further than his predecessors and has removed his subject from the realm of probability to that of almost absolute certainty. Hereafter there can be little question that apart from such influences as the depreciation in gold, or great calamities like the war, the general trend of economic conditions in this country is closely dependent upon cyclical variations in the weather." — ELLSWORTH HUNTINGTON, in the *Geographical Review*.

In reply to the question: "What are the two best books you have read recently," President Butler named, as one of the two books, Professor Moore's *Economic Cycles* because of its being "an original and very stimulating study in economic theory with quick applications to practical business affairs." — NICHOLAS MURRAY BUTLER, in the *New York World*.

"Professor Moore is known among scholars as one of the keenest and most cautious of investigators. . . . His novel methods of investigation constitute an additional claim upon our interest; the problem of the crisis has never yet been approached in precisely this way." — ALVIN S. JOHNSON, in the *New Republic*.

"This book indicates a method of utilizing (economic) data . . . that is worthy of the highest commendation." — ALLEN HAZEN, in the *Engineering News*.

"If the promise of Professor Moore's convincing Essay is fulfilled, economics will become an approximately exact science. . . . If progress is made in the direction of such a goal as a result of this work, it will be the economic contribution of a century, and will usher in a new scientific epoch." — ROY G. BLAKEY, in the *Times Annalist*.

"The agricultural theory of cycles has found a new and brilliant exponent in Professor Henry L. Moore." — WESLEY CLAIR MITCHELL, in the *American Yearbook*.

"If his methods stand the test of experience, and can be widely adopted, the field of business may be revolutionized so far as it concerns the enterpriser because the measuring of the force of underlying, fundamental conditions will become approximately accurate and the function of the enterpriser will thereby be reduced." Magazine published by *Alexander Hamilton Institute*.

"L'auteur a mis à son service des procédés mathématiques et statistiques raffinés et élégants . . . celui-ci a écrit un livre brillant." — UMBERTO RICCI, in *Scientia*.

Laws of Wages

An Essay In Statistical Economics

By HENRY LUDWELL MOORE

Professor of Political Economy in Columbia University

8vo, $1.60

Extract from the Introduction: "In the following chapters I have endeavored to use the newer statistical methods and the more recent economic theory to extract, from data relating to wages, either new truth or else truth in such new form as will admit of its being brought into fruitful relations with the generalizations of economic science."

COMMENTS OF SPECIALISTS

"Professor Moore brings to his task a wide acquaintance with the most difficult parts of the literature of economics and statistics, a full appreciation of its large problems, a judicial spirit and a dignified style." — F. W. TAUSSIG, in the *Quarterly Journal of Economics.*

"Statistics of the ordinary official kind have often served to support the arguments of political economists. But this is the first time, we believe, that the higher statistics, which are founded on the Calculus of Probabilities, have been used on a large scale as a buttress of economic theory." — F. Y. EDGEWORTH, in the *Economic Journal.*

"Professor Moore has broken new ground in a most interesting field, and while we may differ from him in the weight to be attached to this or that result or the interpretation to be placed on some observed coefficient, we may offer cordial congratulations on the work as a whole." — G. Y. YULE, in the *Journal of the Royal Statistical Society.*

"Die Fruchtbarkeit der verwendeten Methode scheint mir durch diese Untersuchungen zweifellos erwiesen, ebenso wie die Erreichbarkeit des Ziels, die Theorie ganz dicht an die Zahlenausdrücke der wirtschaftlichen Tatsachen heranzubringen. Und das ist eine Tat, zu der der Autor nur zu beglückwünschen ist. . . . Hat das Buch auch auf der Hand liegende Fehler — in der Zukunft wird man sich seiner als der ersten klaren, einfachen und zielbewussten Darlegung und Exemplifizierung der Anwendung der 'höheren Statistik' auf ökonomische Probleme dankbar erinnern." — JOSEPH SCHUMPETER, in the *Archiv für Sozialwissenschaft und Sozialpolitik.*

"Non seulement il nous enseigne l'emploi d'une méthode qui dans de certaines limites peut être très féconde. Mais encore son habileté personnelle dans le maniement de cette méthode est très réelle. Il sait scruter les statistiques d'une façon fort pénétrante et exposer les résultats de ses recherches avec beaucoup d'élégance. Le lecteur français en particulier, appréciera l'ingéniosité avec laquelle il tire des statistiques françaises des inductions souvent nouvelles et justes." — ALBERT AFTALION, in the *Revue d'histoire des doctrines économiques.*

"Alcuni dei risultati ottenuti dall'autore, sono nuovi e suggestivi e da essi molte conclusioni si possono trarre (cui l'autore accenna nel capitolo finale della sua opera) sia rispetto alle teorie del salario che rispetto alla politica sociale. Il libro è insomma, ripetiamo, un contributo molto importante all'investigazione scientifica dei fenomeni economici e vorremmo che esso stimolasse parecchi altri studiosi a fare per altre industrie o per altri paesi, recerche analoghe." — CONSTANTINO BRESCIANI TURRONI, in the *Giornale degli Economisti.*